# A Practical Guide to Early Childhood Assessment

# A Practical Guide to Early Childhood Assessment

## Conducting Developmental and Psychological Evaluations in the Early Intervention Program

Scott Mesh, Ph.D. and Joanne Loeb, Ph.D.

Los Niños Press • New York, NY

To order contact:
Los Niños Press
Order Department
2489 Broadway, 2nd Floor
New York, NY 10025
www.losninosservices.com
voice: 1.212.787.9700
fax: 1.212.787.4418

Library of Congress Cataloging-in-Publication Data

Mesh, Scott
A practical guide to early childhood assessment: Conducting developmental and psychological evaluations in the early intervention
program/Scott Mesh, Joanne Loeb

p. cm.
Includes biographical references and index.
ISBN 0-9740878-0-7 (alk. paper)
1. Psychological Assessment 2. Early Childhood

Printed in the United States of America
First Edition

*To Edita and Lenny*

*Thank you for your encouragement and belief in this project*
*from beginning to end.*
*And thank you for being there for us, as always.*

# Acknowledgements

We would like to thank the many families in New York City and Westchester County who have welcomed us into their homes and shared their hopes, aspirations, and concerns for their children with us. They have encouraged us, taught us, laughed with us, cried with us, and have patiently helped us understand and appreciate the small wonders of life—their children.

We would like to thank the many professionals at Los Niños Services who have helped us expand our understanding of early childhood and early intervention. Their ideas and questions have helped us clarify what we know and what we need to learn, and have given us the incentive to complete this manual.

We especially wish to thank the following people who have encouraged us in this endeavor, and who have reviewed the manuscript and provided feedback to us. We credit them with positive suggestions and take responsibility for any shortcomings in the final draft. We wish to thank Barbara Alexander, Agnes Alvarez, Oribel Botero, Francia Brito, Edita Diaz, Lourdes Diaz, David Glenwick, Lenny Malter, Sally Mesh, Ellen Monane, Molly Nozyce, Camilia Negron, Claudia Olave-Guillermo, Nelida Portella, Ozgul Uzgun, and Chun Zhang.

We appreciate the work of our layout design done by Jonathan Gullery, and the printing done by booksjustbooks.com. Thank you for working quickly and efficiently to enhance the quality of our work and making it more readable and accessible.

Finally, we thank our families for putting up with our keyboard tapping late into the night, on the weekends, and in the wee hours of the morning. Thank you Edita Diaz, Lenny Malter, Maya Isabella, Sofia, Zachary, Emily, and Jonah for your understanding and support, and for allowing us to devote many hours to this project so it could be seen through to completion. A special thanks goes to Emperatriz Bravo, Gonzolo Diaz, Lourdes Diaz, Monica Diaz, and Marielena Diaz for helping with child care so we could work on this project.

# About the Authors

**Scott Mesh, Ph.D.**, is a bilingual clinical psychologist and Executive Director of Los Niños Services. He is an international speaker on bilingual early childhood assessment and specializes in developmental and psychological assessment of Spanish-speaking children. He has served as an adjunct professor at Long Island University, Yeshiva University, Queens College, and the New York Medical College. He co-founded the American Psychological Association of Graduate Students in 1988 with Dr. David Pilon, of Halifax, Canada. Dr. Mesh studied Spanish in Seville, Spain, and received his bachelor's degree in psychology, with honors, from the University of Michigan. He received his doctorate in clinical psychology from St. John's University. With Edita Diaz, M.S. Ed., he co-founded Los Niños Services in 1998. Together they have two children and make their home in New York City.

**Joanne Loeb, Ph.D.**, is a bilingual clinical psychologist and Training Coordinator of Los Niños Services. She studied in Quito, Ecuador, and received her master's degree in developmental psychology from Teachers College and her doctorate in clinical psychology from Yeshiva University. Previously, she worked with young children at the Children's Evaluation and Rehabilitation Center at the Albert Einstein College of Medicine and served as an adjunct professor at Yeshiva University. She specializes in developmental and psychological evaluations of young Spanish-speaking children and the assessment of autism and pervasive developmental disorder in young children. She lives in the New York area with her husband and three children.

# Contents

# *About This Book*

When we started working in this field, there were no hands-on manuals explaining exactly how an evaluator performs evaluations in the Early Intervention Program (EIP). We had previous experience and training in working with children but did not know the specifics of how to evaluate infants and toddlers within the EIP. This book is intended to fill the need for practical information about the evaluation process, particularly for teachers and psychologists conducting developmental and psychological evaluations of children under age three. We discuss the issues that arise in performing early childhood evaluations and writing evaluation reports, and we provide many suggestions for other evaluators. Our ideas for this guide reflect our experiences working with many young children and their families in the New York City metropolitan area. We have worked with children from many social, cultural, religious, and ethnic backgrounds. Some children have parents who are pediatricians, lawyers, and business owners; others belong to immigrant families with parents who are trying to make a living cleaning houses or gardening. Many of the children and families we work with are bilingual, most often speaking Spanish and English, and we try to address all of their concerns in the evaluation process.

This guide describes the process of conducting evaluations for the Early Intervention Program, a program with specific rules and requirements. However, many of the issues we discuss may also be relevant for other infant and toddler programs, and for evaluating young children privately. In our experience, and as expressed through the philosophy of Early Intervention, we have found that it is helpful to work in the child's natural environment as much as possible. This guide therefore emphasizes home-based evaluations of young children. Many infants and toddlers are also evaluated in clinics, offices, hospital and day care settings. Even though conducting evaluations in those settings is different, we hope that many of the issues presented in this guide will be relevant for those who work in those settings as well.

In order to make the text more readable we have made some literary choices. This guide is written primarily for the professional who is, or will be, evaluating infants and toddlers under the Early Intervention Program. Thus, when we use the word "you," we intend to mean "you the evaluator." When the word "we" is used in the text, it refers to ourselves, the authors. In addition, instead of using "he/she" to refer to the parent or caregiver, we use "she." Although we do tend to work with more mothers than fathers, we acknowledge that many fathers are actively involved in childcare and with their children. We have also decided to refer to the child as "he." This will allow the reader to determine more easily whether we are referring to the parent (she) or the child (he). We understand that the child may have one parent, both parents, a guardian, foster parent, or other caregiver. For convenience, we have often chosen to use the term parent, although we acknowledge that children often have both parents, and may have different kinds of caregivers. We hope these choices allow for easier reading of this material.

This book is a practical guide to performing evaluations and writing reports. It assumes that the reader already has a background in early childhood development. For additional information regarding early childhood development and assessment, please see our list of resources and references. Also, you can refer to the many texts on early childhood development for more detailed information and theories of early childhood development.

There is a growing need for interested and qualified evaluators in the Early Intervention Program. We hope that with the use of this guide, more professionals will become interested in developing this new area of expertise. Conducting early childhood assessments can be a very rewarding experience, as you can be instrumental in beginning to provide help to children and families. We hope the guide helps to make the assessment process more manageable and more enjoyable for evaluators. We are also interested in hearing from readers about what you found most helpful in this guide, as well as any comments you may have. Feel free to e-mail us through the Los Ninos Services website: www.losninosservices.com.

Finally, this book represents the sole opinions of the authors, who are not speaking on behalf of any county, state, or federal early intervention program. Note that the exact rules and regulations by which the EIP operate vary by county, state and country. In addition, rules and regulations change over time. Thus, you must contact your local EIP to learn about the latest rules, regulations and procedures.

# Glossary

AE                 age equivalent

CA                 chronological age

CPR                concerns, priorities and resources

CPSE               Committee on Preschool Special Education

DSM IV             Diagnostic and Statistical Manual of the
                   American Psychiatric Association (4th edition)

EIOD               Early Intervention Official Designee

EIP                Early Intervention Program

FA                 functional age

LRE                least restrictive environment

ICD 9              International Classification of Disorders (9th Edition)

IDEA               Individual with Disabilities Education Act

IFSP               Individualized Family Service Plan

PDD                pervasive developmental disorder

PDD NOS            pervasive developmental disorder,
                   not otherwise specified

SD                 standard deviation

# Overview

In recent years there has been an increasing interest in early childhood development, as research has demonstrated the importance of the first years for determining the course of development across a lifetime (Shonkoff & Meisels, 2000). With this new knowledge has come an awareness of the need for identifying those infants and toddlers who are not achieving optimal growth and are at risk for future developmental or interpersonal problems. Only after these children have been evaluated and identified with developmental delays or disorders can the appropriate interventions be provided. Unfortunately, few training opportunities exist for those professionals interested in learning how to evaluate very young children. Graduate programs and specialized trainings in education and psychology tend to devote little time to the study of children from birth to age three. Those professionals interested in learning how to perform early childhood evaluations must be creative in looking for the proper educational opportunities. With this guide, we hope to provide some of the background, which we believe is essential, for developing proficiency in early childhood assessment.

It is important for evaluators of young children to be knowledgeable in a variety of different areas. Many early childhood evaluators work under the auspices of the Early Intervention Program (EIP). This program has been established in most of the United States, and EIP, or similar programs, have also been established in a number of other countries as well (Kamerman, 2000). This manual will focus on the EIP as established in the U.S., and it reflects our experiences in New York State. The implementation of the EIP varies somewhat in different states and localities, and exact program requirements and procedures should be obtained from your own state and locality. The EIP provides evaluations and services to young children (ages birth to three) with developmental disabilities and developmental delays and is free to parents. In order to perform effective early childhood evaluations, professionals must be well informed about the guidelines and requirements of the Early Intervention Program.

Working with infants and toddlers involves a different set of expectations and clinical skills than those needed to work with older children. Professionals must be comfortable with very young children who have limited verbal skills and can be impulsive, emotional, and unpredictable. Developing an expertise in this area also involves learning about early childhood development and knowing the important milestones achieved during the first years of life, as well as the developmental delays and disorders that can be identified in early childhood.

Evaluating very young children means working closely with parents and other family members. Open communication with parents through each step of the evaluation process is very important. This helps to keep the parents informed and assures their input and support during the process. In addition, evaluating young children involves working in a variety of settings. Services are preferably provided in the child's natural environment, such as the child's home, a relative's home, or a day care center. Working in different settings requires a strong sense of professional identity on the part of evaluators, as they are often isolated from other professionals and do not have a consistent place of work. Early Intervention professionals may have to make an extra effort to seek out opportunities for professional development, training, and consultation.

This guide will describe the EIP and give some background on early childhood development. It also will offer many practical tips for performing evaluations and writing evaluation reports. Although we can only briefly describe the important developmental changes that occur in early childhood, we hope that evaluators reading this manual will make use of the resources identified here to continue expanding their knowledge of early childhood development and the EIP. We hope that the many practical suggestions we offer will help evaluators make thorough assessments and write clear, coherent reports that fulfill the requirements of the EIP. The manual covers the following topics:

Chapter 1. *The Early Intervention Program:* History, philosophy, guidelines, and regulations of the Early Intervention Program.

Chapter 2. *Understanding Developmental Delays and Disorders in Early Childhood:* Normal early childhood development, important early developmental milestones, delays versus disorders, criteria for eligibility under the EIP.

Chapter 3. *General Considerations When Conducting Early Childhood Evaluations:* Individual versus team evaluations, the referral, scheduling issues, parents' feelings about the evaluation process.

Chapter 4. *Beginning the Evaluation:* Safety issues, initial contact with the family, family culture, obtaining consent, use of a laptop computer, explaining the evaluation process, establishing rapport, the sequence of the evaluation.

Chapter 5. *The Parent Interview:* Interviewing style and techniques, suggested topics and outline for parent interview, how to work with the parent to obtain a full understanding of the child.

Chapter 6. *Formal Testing, Tests and Measures:* Setting up for the formal testing, involving parents, eliciting optimal performance, eliciting cooperation from the child, establishing rapport, involving siblings, establishing validity of the testing, early childhood tests and measures.

Chapter 7. *Informal Assessment of Behavior, Social-Emotional Functioning, and Play:* Behavioral observations, social-emotional functioning, play assessment, play scales.

Chapter 8. *Closing Discussion with Parents:* Last questions, situational factors, informing parents of your impressions and recommendations.

Chapter 9. *How to Identify Autism and Pervasive Developmental Disorder NOS (PDD) in Young Children:* Diagnostic criteria, the parent interview, rating scales and other measures, clinical observations, challenges of assessing autism, discussing autism with parents, common parent questions and suggested answers.

Chapter 10. *Writing Early intervention Reports:* Purpose of the reports, common report writing problems and solutions, suggested report outline, writing about autism and pervasive developmental disorders, working with an evaluation agency.

*Appendix l. Medical Disorders of Early Childhood*

*Appendix ll. Common Childhood Behavioral and Social Disorders*

*Resources:* Organizations, journals, newsletters, and websites that provide additional information on early childhood assessment.

*I.*

# The Early Intervention Program

## Description

The Early Intervention Program (EIP) provides services to children age 0-3 with developmental delays or developmental disabilities and their families. Children are eligible for Early Intervention if they have a significant developmental delay, or if they have a diagnosed condition with a high probability of developmental delay (see Chapter II for eligibility criteria). The EIP is administered in each state by a lead agency, which is typically the Department of Health or the Department of Education. The program is voluntary and free of charge to families. Typically, the child's insurance covers a portion of the costs for EIP services. Any remaining costs are paid for by the government. However, as of this writing, there is discussion in New York State about possibly changing the reimbursement procedures.

## History

The EIP for infants and toddlers with disabilities and their families was created by Congress in 1986 through Public Law 99-457 and was later reauthorized under the Individuals with Disabilities Education Act (IDEA). Since 1986, many states have developed their own Early Intervention Programs. For example, in New York State on July 1, 1993, the EIP was made available to families through Article 25 of the Public Health Law, which established the Department of Health as the lead agency for the program. The program is relatively new, and is still in the process of development. In 1999 the New York State Department of Health established the first set of clinical practice guidelines on Communication Disorders and Autism/Pervasive Developmental Disorders (New York State Department of Health, 1999) with the aim of increasing the quality of the evaluation and intervention process, and to help parents and professionals better understand these and other disorders.

## *Philosophy*

The mission of the EIP is to "identify and evaluate as early as possible those infants and toddlers whose healthy development is compromised and provide for appropriate intervention to improve child and family development" (p. xiv, New York State Department of Health, 1999). Under the EIP, the preference is to provide evaluations in "natural settings in the community where peers are typically found" (p. xiii, New York State Dept of Health, 1999). These settings may include the child's home, a relative or babysitter's home, community centers, religious centers, libraries or schools, depending on the situation of the particular child and family. When possible, working with the child in a natural, rather than in a clinical, setting has been recommended by the EIP. The rationale is that the child usually feels more comfortable and typically is more cooperative in a natural setting and may therefore exhibit more optimal behaviors. For very young children who spend most of their time at home and are most comfortable at home, the home-based evaluation also provides a more accurate picture of the child's typical functioning. Providing evaluations in community-based centers is also encouraged, because it is thought to encourage families to become more involved in community activities.

Parents are an essential part of the EIP, as they are closest to the child and most able to monitor the child's developmental progress. Interventions should be provided in a way that supports parents' efforts to care for and nurture their children. It is important for parents' concerns and priorities to be addressed, and parents should be relied on as important sources of information about their child's development. When services are provided, parents should participate in sessions and be educated in how to work with their child at home to facilitate the child's development. Involving parents in the evaluation process also facilitates the child's participation, allows the child to feel more at ease, and gives a more accurate and complete assessment of the child's abilities. (For a white paper addressing a range of evaluations issues, see *The Westchester County Local Coordinating Council*, 1999).

The philosophy of the EIP is that evaluations should focus on a child's strengths and optimal functioning. This means creating an environment that allows the child to perform at his best. Working with the child on the floor, using the family's dominant language, allowing for breaks, and involving family members are all examples of ways to facilitate optimal functioning. It is also important to identify the child's areas of strength to help facilitate his development in other areas. In addition, an important goal of the EIP is to help strengthen families.

## *Differences between Early Intervention and Special Education*

Once a child has completed the EIP program, they may be eligible for services under the Committee for Preschool Special Education (CPSE). Although the EIP and the CPSE both provide interventions for young children, there are significant differences between the two programs. In the United States the EIP is typically administered through the county in which the child resides, usually by either the Department of Health or the Department of Education. The EIP is based on a belief that providing services at an early age can help avoid the need for intervention later on in life. The EIP attempts to provide services in a natural setting, such as a home or day care center, although some children attend center-based programs. Professionals in the EIP work directly with the family, helping them to promote their child's development. The EIP also provides an initial and ongoing service coordinator to establish and maintain the child's service plan and to ensure that the child receives the appropriate services. In summary, the EIP is family focused, services are preferably provided in the natural environment, the philosophy is to provide intervention as early as possible, and service coordination is provided to every family.

The EIP is different from the CPSE, which provides special education services for children ages 3 and up. CPSE services are provided through the Committee on Special Education in each school district, under the direction of the Board of Education. The philosophy of special education is that children should be given services in the "least restrictive environment" (LRE). This means that services should be provided in an educational setting "close to home with other children of the same age who do not have disabilities" (New York State Education Department, 2003). Parent involvement is different in the CPSE than it is in the EIP. Children over the age of 3 who become eligible for special education are often placed in preschools, in which parent participation is limited. Parents do not have the opportunity to see their children working with the professionals on a regular basis as they do when the child receives home-based services under the EIP. Parents need to take a larger role in monitoring their own child's progress as there are no service coordinators to advocate for them under the CPSE. In summary, special education services tend to be child-focused, they are provided in centers or schools, the philosophy is to provide the "least restrictive environment" for services, and parents have a larger role in advocating for their children, as no service coordination is provided.

## *Types of Early Intervention (EI) Evaluations*

1) Audiological – assesses the child's hearing ability.
2) Developmental – assesses the child's learning and overall development, including the five domains of functioning (cognitive, communication, adaptive, motor, social).
3) Feeding – assesses the ability of the child to chew, swallow, drink and eat.
4) Occupational Therapy – assesses self-help skills, adaptive behavior, play, sensory, fine motor skills.
5) Physical Therapy – assesses gross motor development.
6) Psychological – assesses child's social-emotional development, behavior, and other issues, as relevant to the referral reason.
7) Speech and Language – assesses communication skills, oral-motor development.
8) Vision – assesses child's eyesight.

## *Types of Early Intervention Services*

1) Assistive Technology – provides equipment and services that help children participate more fully in activities such as playing, communicating, eating, or moving.
2) Audiology – helps with hearing difficulties.
3) Family Training, Counseling, Parent Support Groups – provides parenting strategies, teaches parents about age appropriate expectations, addresses family needs.

4) Nursing – provides nursing care for children with medical needs.
5) Nutrition – focuses on feeding skills, feeding problems, food habits, and food preferences.
6) Occupational Therapy – focuses on fine motor skills, adaptive functioning, and sensory issues.
7) Physical Therapy – focuses on gross motor skills.
8) Psychological Services – helps children and their families with behavioral and social-emotional problems.
9) Service Coordination – helps advocates for families, assists them through the evaluation process, obtains any needed services, and monitors service delivery.
10) Social Work – addresses needs of family and helps family find resources in the community.
11) Special Instruction - facilitates child's learning and development.
12) Speech-Language Pathology – stimulates the child's communication, feeding, and oral-motor skills.
13) Vision Services – helps visually impaired or blind children learn to adapt to their environment.
14) Health Services – as needed for the child to benefit from other EI services.
15) Transportation – can be provided to children so they can obtain EI services.

## *Bilingual Evaluations*

Under the EIP, evaluations should be done in the "primary" language of the family, meaning the language that the family uses most often when speaking to the child. Evaluators who are not bilingual must use a translator to assist them. The translator can be another professional or a family member. Evaluation reports should indicate the child's dominant language, what languages were used in the evaluation and how competent the child was in each. Any standardized instruments used should ideally be normed on the child's cultural-linguistic group. However, few standardized instruments are actually normed on non-English speaking children, and the administration procedures typically must be modified for bilingual populations. You should also rely heavily on clinical observations and the parents' report (The Westchester County Local Early Intervention Coordinating Council, 1999).

## How EIP Works

Anyone can refer a child to the EIP. Parents can refer their own child, or pediatricians, as well as other professionals, can make a referral. Referrals by professionals should be done with the parents' full approval and consent. Suspicion that a child has a developmental delay or disorder is sufficient to warrant a referral to the program. Referrals are made by calling the EIP in the county in which the family resides. Once the EIP has been contacted, the EIP assigns an initial service coordinator to oversee the evaluation process and to follow the family through the Individualized Family Service Plan (IFSP). The initial service coordinator (1) starts the process by calling or visiting the family; (2) talks with the family about their concerns regarding their child's development; (3) receives consent from the family to begin the evaluation process; (4) provides the family with a list of evaluation agencies in their county, so that the family can choose an evaluation site; and (5) contacts the evaluation agency and informs them that an evaluation is needed.

Evaluations are usually conducted in a "natural setting," such as the child's home, a relative or babysitter's home, or a day care center. At times they are conducted in a clinical setting. At a minimum, two evaluations are performed. The initial multidisciplinary evaluations are referred to as the "core evaluation." The core evaluation consists of a general evaluation (either a developmental or psychological evaluation), which covers the five areas of development (cognitive, communication, adaptive, social and motor) and one evaluation in the area of concern. Additional evaluations (called supplemental evaluations) may be performed if there are other areas of concern. Any evaluator may recommend additional evaluations to further assess other areas of development.

Once the evaluations are complete, the reports are sent to the parents, the initial service coordinator and the EIP. The initial service coordinator then coordinates the scheduling of a meeting to develop the Individualized Family Service Plan (IFSP). This is called the IFSP meeting. This meeting should occur within 45 days from the child's referral to the EIP. The IFSP meeting includes the a parent or caretaker, another person chosen by the parent to assist or support her, the initial service coordinator, a representative of the evaluation team, and a representative from the EIP known as the Early Intervention Official Designee (EIOD). During the IFSP meeting, the participants review the evaluations and other information gathered about the child. They discuss the family's concerns, priorities and resources (see Chapter 5). The goal of this meeting is to determine the interventions necessary to facilitate the child's development and to help the family. The goal is for all of the IFSP meeting participants to cooperatively agree upon the final IFSP document. During the IFSP meeting, the family also chooses an ongoing service coordinator who will help to implement the IFSP. The ongoing service coordinator helps the family obtain the services they need. They find the service providers, if they have not yet been identified, and work to ensure that the services are provided in a timely manner. They are responsible for establishing subsequent planning meetings, including six-month reviews and annual evaluations. The ongoing service coordinator implements any changes in the service plan.

As the child approaches age 3, the family is offered an opportunity to have him evaluated under the Committee on Preschool Special Education (CPSE). If the family agrees to this evaluation, the child's progress can be thoroughly assessed and a determination can be made about whether the child still needs services. Services can then be provided through the special education program, if approved. Children become ineligible for Early Intervention at the end of August or December of the year in which they turn 3, depending on their birth dates. Children born from January through August age out of the EIP on August 31 following their third birthday, and those children born from September 1 through December 31 age out of the EIP on December 31 following their third birthday. Thus, if a child turns 3 June 25, then their age out date will be August 31. If the child turns 3 on September 28th then the age out date would be December 31, and so forth.

## The Role of the Evaluator in the EIP

As an evaluator in the EIP, you have four important roles. First, you make an assessment of the child's development based on a combination of the information obtained from parents, and the results of your formal and informal assessments. In your report, you describe the child's skills in each area of development and identify any developmental delays or disabilities. Second, your evaluation, along with other evaluations, will determine if the child qualifies for any Early Intervention services. This involves providing your determination of the extent to which the child is performing below, at, or above age level, based on test results, professional opinion, or both. Third, you educate the family in a variety of different ways. You give feedback regarding the child's strengths and any developmental delays or disabilities, which you identify. Evaluators can also inform the family about Early Intervention and what to expect from the evaluation process. Fourth, you may make recommendations for intervention and perhaps for other evaluations. You can recommend intervention only in your area of expertise. However, you can recommend evaluations in other areas, which you believe need further investigation. For example, if you are a teacher, but notice that the child is unstable on his feet compared to other children his age, you may recommend a physical therapy evaluation. However, it would be the role of the physical therapist to recommend any physical therapy services, if needed.

*II.*

# Understanding Developmental Delays and Disorders in Early Childhood

## Learning About Normal Early Childhood Development

A background in normal early childhood development is essential for conducting early childhood assessments. Knowledge about the many theories of cognitive, social, communication, motor and adaptive development, and a familiarity with research in early childhood, provides a background for understanding what is "normal." It is also helpful to have experience working with young children of different ages. Only when you know what "normal" development is (within a broad range) can you determine what is not "normal" (either delayed or disordered). You must compare the child you are evaluating with what is "normal" for that child's age, in order to determine with some confidence that the child has developmental delays. It is helpful to use developmental charts, such as the one we provide below, as a quick reference for important developmental milestones. They should not, however, substitute for the more extensive training in early childhood development, which you must have to perform early childhood assessments effectively. The chart presented below covers the five domains of development from ages 6 months to 36 months, and is composed of information gathered from the following sources: Assessment Log and Developmental Progress Chart for The Carolina Curriculum for Children with Special Needs (Johnson-Martin & Attermeier, 1990), Child Development Inventory (Ireton, 1992), Hawaii Early Learning Profile (VORT Corporation, 1995), Vineland Adaptive Behavior Scales (Sparrow, Balla & Cicchetti, 1984).

# Developmental Milestones Chart

## By 6 months

### Cognition:

Uses hands and mouth to explore objects
Turns eyes and head to sound of hidden voice
Localizes sound with eyes
Finds a partially hidden object

### Communication:

Fixes gaze on face
Responds to name by looking for voice
Regularly localizes sound
Coos, gurgles, chuckles, laughs
Says a vowel-consonant combination such as "ah goo"

### Socialization:

Social smile
Vocalizes in response to adult talk and smile
Demands social attention
Vocalizes pleasure and displeasure
Distinguishes mother from others

### Daily Living Skills:

Reacts to sight of bottle or breast
Comforts self with thumb or pacifier

### Motor:

Lifts head and chest when lying on stomach
Turns over when lying on stomach
Holds head in line with body when pulled to sitting
Bears almost all weight on legs
Looks and reaches for faces or toys
Picks up toy with one hand

## By 12 months

### Cognition:

Plays peek-a-boo
Follows trajectory of fast moving objects
Looks for family members or pets when named
Retains two of three objects
Turns head and shoulders to find hidden sound
Imitates familiar and new gesture

### Communication:

Initiates vocalization
Different vocalizations for different states
Recognizes familiar people
Reciprocal social games (peek a boo, pat a cake)
Imitates familiar sounds and actions
Cries when parent leaves
Reduplicative babbling (baba, mama)
Attracts attention by vocalizing
Shakes head "no"
Waves "bye"
Indicates requests clearly
Coordinates actions betweens adults and objects

### Socialization:

Reaches for familiar person
Plays social games (peek a boo)
Plays patty cake
Shows anxiety over separation from mother
Smiles at mirror image
Extends toy to show others
Explores environment
Shows like and dislike for certain people, objects, places

### Daily Living Skills:

Holds own bottle
Feeds self a cracker
Picks up spoon by handle

### Motor:

Crawls around on hands and knees
Goes from sitting to prone
Lowers to sitting from standing
Cruises, walks around furniture or crib while holding on
Picks up small objects; precise thumb and finger grasp

## By 18 months

**Cognition:**

> Turns two or three pages at a time
> Identifies self in the mirror
> Identifies one body part
> Recognizes and points to four animal pictures

**Communication:**

> Begins single word production
> Requestsing objects, such as food, with words
> Uses ritual words: bye, hi, thank you, please
> Protests: says "no," shakes head
> Comments: points to object and vocalizes
> Acknowledges: makes eye contact and vocalizes

**Socialization:**

> Gives kisses or hugs
> Greets people with "hi"
> Gives toy to familiar adult
> Displays independent behavior
> Displays frequent tantrum behavior
> Begins to show sense of humor
> Plays ball cooperatively
> Shows toy preferences

**Daily Living Skills:**

> Indicates discomfort over soiled pants
> Lifts cup to mouth and drinks
> Feeds self with spoon
> Insists on doing things by self, such as feeding

**Motor:**

> Stands without support
> Walks without help
> Runs
> Stacks 2 two or more blocks
> Picks up 2 two small toys in one hand

## By 24 months

### Cognition:

Points to several clothing items on request
Matches sound to animals
Matches object to picture
Assembles four nesting blocks
Identifies three body parts
Recognizes self in photograph
Uses Play-Doh and paints

### Communication:

Uses mostly words to communicate
Begins to use two-word combinations
Uses word combinations with relational meanings
(daddy shoe, more juice)
Has at least 50 words
Follows two-part instruction

### Socialization:

Sometimes says "no"
Shows sympathy for other children and tries to comfort
Shows jealousy of attention given to others
Shows a wide variety of emotions
Engages in parallel play
Defends possessions

### Daily Living Skills:

Eats with fork
Eats with spoon, spilling little
Takes off front-opening jacket or shirt
Removes shoes when laces undone
Helps with simple household tasks

### Motor:

Kicks a ball forward
Runs well, seldom falls
Walks up and down stairs alone, both feet on step
Builds towers of four or more blocks
Turns pages of picture book, one at a time

## By 30 months

### Cognition:

Understands concept of one
Recognizes familiar adult in picture
Engages in simple make-believe activities
Obeys two-part commands
Matches shapes and colors

### Communication:

Understands many action verbs
Names most pictures of familiar objects

### Daily Living Skills:

Understands common dangers: stairs, glass, strange animals
Indicates need to use the toilet

### Socialization:

Plays with other children using dolls, cars, blocks
Displays dependent behavior
Frustration tantrums peak
Dramatizes using doll
Becomes aware of sex differences
May develop sudden fears, especially of large animals

### Motor:

Opens doors by turning the knobs
Climbs on play equipment
Jumps from 8 to 14 inches
Catches large ball
Scribbles with circular motion
Draws or copies vertical lines

## By 36 months

### Cognition:

Matches similar pictures of objects
Sorts shapes
Completes 3-piece puzzle
Stacks rings in correct order
Points to larger or smaller of two spoons
Understands concept of two
Sorts colors and points to several colors when named
Identifies longer stick
Understands all common verbs and some adjectives

### Communication:

Engages in short dialogues
Uses language in imaginative way
Provides descriptive details
Links unrelated ideas and story elements
Begins to include articles and word endings
Understands four prepositions

### Socialization:

Role plays in pretend games such as: mom, dad, teacher
Shows independence
Begins to obey and respect simple rules

### Daily Living Skills:

Pulls pants down with assistance
Dresses self with help
Pulls pants up with assistance
Wipes nose with assistance
Pours liquid from small container
Uses toilet with assistance
Washes and dries hands
Buttons large buttons

### Motor:

Stands on one foot without support
Walks up and down steps, alternating feet
Draws or copies vertical lines
Cuts with small scissors

## Early Childhood Developmental Delays Versus Disorders

Children may present with either a developmental delay or a developmental disorder. In order to make an accurate assessment of the child, it is important to understand the difference between a developmental delay and a developmental disorder. You also need to be familiar with the different types of developmental disorders that can be identified in early childhood.

A delay is when a child is behind in his development and is functioning more like a normal child of a younger chronological age. Some examples of behaviors that might indicate a **developmental delay** are:

> A 1-year-old who does not sit unsupported
> A 2-year-old who does not say any words
> A 3-year-old who does not drink from a cup independently

Sometimes children will be delayed in their development and also have a developmental disorder. Children with a developmental disorder function in a manner that is atypical at any age. The following are a few examples of behaviors, which might indicate a **developmental disorder:**

> A 1-year-old who does not make eye contact
> A 2-year-old who makes frequent grunting sounds
>     or high pitched squeals
> A 3-year-old who frequently walks on his toes

## Determining Eligibility for Services

Determining eligibility for services involves calculating whether the child is sufficiently delayed to meet the eligibility requirements for Early Intervention. This determination can be based on the results of formal measures, on your professional opinion, or both. When possible, use norm referenced tests instead of criterion referenced tests. Eligibility is determined based on the results of all evaluations.

Often your professional opinion will be in agreement with the results of the formal measures. If so, you would state the child's scores on the formal measures and then present observations, which support these findings. Sometimes, however, you may feel that the formal measures do not give an accurate estimate of the child's level of functioning. In this case, your impressions of the child may override the results of the test scores.

You can use your professional opinion when you believe that the formal testing does not accurately portray the child's skills. For example, a child may score at age level in the area of socialization because he is sociable and initiates interactions with others. Yet, he may have some behavioral problems, such as tantrums and aggressive behavior, which are not picked up by the tests you are using. If the parent reports a concern about his behavior, or if you observe some significant behavioral difficulties, you may determine that based on this information the child does qualify for services. In this case you need to use your professional opinion to support one of the criteria for eligibility (see below). For example, you could state, "based on professional opinion the child is estimated to be performing more than 25% below age level on social skills, and services are recommended to address social difficulties."

Professional opinion can also be used when the child is not cooperative with the formal testing, but based on other sources of information (such as parent interview, interview ratings, play or informal assessment), you can make an accurate assessment of the child's functioning. There are also situations in which the child was very tired on the day of testing. Perhaps the parent said so, you observed the child yawning throughout the testing, and then the child went to sleep when you finished testing. You may determine that the child's performance was likely a significant underestimate of his typical functioning since he was tired on the day of testing. Alternatively, a child might perform "within normal limits" on a test of motor development. You observe that this 16-month-old child is walking, which, according to this test, means that the child is approximately on age level. However, the child just started walking a few weeks ago, is falling frequently and tripping, and shows very poor balance and coordination. Despite the child being able to perform the expected tasks of his age (e.g., walking), the child is not performing them with the coordination expected. You can then report that, in your professional opinion, this child is estimated to be performing below age level, and you may recommend further testing from a physical or occupational therapist.

## Calculating a Developmental Delay

A child qualifies for services under EIP if he has a significant enough developmental delay. The delay needs to be reported as either a percent delay or as a standard deviation below the mean. A delay will qualify a child for services if any of the following criteria are met:

> 2.0 or more standard deviations below the mean
> (in 1 developmental area)
> 1.5 or more standard deviations below the mean
> (in two or more areas)
> 12-month delay (in 1 area)
> 33% or more delay (in 1 area)
> 25% or more delay (in two or more areas)

It is up to the evaluator to determine which eligibility criteria to use (either standard deviation, percent delay, or months delayed) in the determination of eligibility.

---

### Percent Delay

To calculate the percent delay, use the following formula:

$1 - FA/CA$

FA = Functional Age level (obtained from the test, also known as the age equivalent)

CA = Chronological Age of the child

* Note: You should round up or down to the next highest (or lowest) percentage point (e.g., round 16.7% up to 17%; round 23.45% down to 23%)

---

## Examples:

1.  A child is two years old and performs at the 1-year-old level on a test. The formula would be:

    $1 - 1/2 = 1/2$, or 50%

    Thus, this child has a 50% delay.

2.  A child is age 26 months and performs at the 16-month-old level on a test. The

formula would be as follows: $1 - 16/26 = .38$, or 38% delay in that area. This is sufficient alone to qualify for Early Intervention services.

3. A child is age 32 months and performs at the 28-month level. The formula would be as follows: $1 - 28/32 = .125$, or 12.5% delayed. This result would mean that the child is ineligible for services in this area.

4. Let's take a child who is age 24 months. You completed the Hawaii Early Learning Profile (HELP) with this child. The child's scores were as follows:

| | |
|---|---|
| Cognitive | 20 months |
| Social | 18 months |
| Adaptive | 18 months |
| Communication | 16 months |
| Motor Skills | 22 months |

How delayed is this child in terms of percent delay?

Here is how you would calculate the percent delays for each area of this test.

| | | |
|---|---|---|
| Cognitive | 20 months | $1 - 20/24 = 16\%$ delay |
| Social | 18 months | $1 - 18/24 = 25\%$ delay |
| Adaptive | 18 months | $1 - 18/24 = 25\%$ delay |
| Communication | 16 months | $1 - 16/24 = 33\%$ delay |
| Motor Skills | 22 months | $1 - 22/24 = 8\%$ delay |

This child demonstrates a delay of 33% in the communication area. This delay alone is sufficient for eligibility. However, even if this child were not delayed in the communication area, the child has sufficient delays (25%) in two areas (social, adaptive), to qualify for services.

5. Let's take another child who is age 24 months. You completed the Hawaii Early Learning Profile (HELP) with this child. The child's scores were as follows:

| | |
|---|---|
| Cognitive | 20 months |
| Social | 19 months |
| Adaptive | 20 months |
| Communication | 18 months |
| Motor Skills | 22 months |

How delayed is this child in terms of percent delay?

Here is how you would calculate the percent delays for each area of this test.

| | | |
|---|---|---|
| Cognitive | 20 months | $1 - 20/24 = 16\%$ delay |
| Social | 19 months | $1 - 19/24 = 21\%$ delay |
| Adaptive | 20 months | $1 - 20/24 = 16\%$ delay |

| | | |
|---|---|---|
| Communication | 18 months | 1 – 18/24 = 25% delay |
| Motor Skills | 22 months | 1 – 22/24 = 8% delay |

This child is slightly developmentally delayed in all areas and the child demonstrates a delay of 25% in the communication area. However, this delay is not sufficient to be eligible for services in the EIP.

**Standard Deviation**. A standard deviation (SD) is obtained from a table in the test manual. Not all tests report standard deviations based on a child's score. Some tests only use functional age equivalents, and other tests do not have any norms.

## Examples:

1. A child is two years old, and has a SD of -2 on the Bayley Scales of Infant Development. This child would qualify for services based on the results of this test alone.

2. A child is age 26 months and has a SD of -1.5 on the Bayley Scales of Infant Development. This would not be sufficient alone to qualify for Early Intervention services. The child would need to have a SD of at least -1.5 in another area of development, or at least 25% delay in another area to qualify for services.

3. Let's take a child who is age 24 months. You completed several tests and the results are as follows:

| | |
|---|---|
| Cognitive | SD = -1.5 |
| Social | AE = 20 months |
| Adaptive | AE = 18 months |
| Communication | AE = 16 months |
| Motor Skills | AE = 22 months |

How delayed is this child, and does the child qualify for services?

Here is how you would calculate the delays for each area of this test.

| | | |
|---|---|---|
| Cognitive | SD = -1.5 (this does not need any further calculation) | |
| Social | AE = 20 months | 1 – 20/24 = 16% delay |
| Adaptive | AE = 18 months | 1 – 18/24 = 25% delay |
| Communication | AE = 19 months | 1 – 19/24 = 21% delay |
| Motor Skills | AE = 22 months | 1 – 22/24 = 8% delay |

This child demonstrates a delay of 25% in the adaptive area and is -1.5SD from the mean. This child is eligible for services, since the child has a sufficient delay in two areas (cognitive and adaptive).

4.   Here is an example of an 18-month-old child. You completed the Bayley Scales of Infant Development and the Vineland Scales of Adaptive Behavior. The child's scores were as follows:

| | |
|---|---|
| Cognitive | SD = -1.3 |
| Social | AE = 16 months |
| Adaptive | AE = 18 months |
| Communication | AE = 15 months |
| Motor Skills | AE = 20 months |

Does the child qualify for services?

Here is how you would calculate the delays for each area of this test.

| | | |
|---|---|---|
| Cognitive | SD = -1.3 (this does not need any further calculation) | |
| Social | AE = 16 months | 1 – 16/18 = 11% delay |
| Adaptive | AE = 18 months | 1 – 18/18 = 0% delay |
| Communication | AE = 15 months | 1 – 15/18 = 17% delay |
| Motor Skills | AE = 21 months | 1 – 21/18 = 17% above age level |

This child is not performing more than 1.5SD below the mean, nor is the child performing 25% or more delay in any area. Therefore, the child would not qualify for early intervention services.

***Standard Scores***. Standard scores are used for some tests, such as the Bayley Scales of Infant Development (see chapter 6). The standard score is useful, as you can compare the standard score from one test with the same kind of standard score from another test. Many, but not all, tests have a mean of 100 (of the standard score) and a standard deviation of 15 standard score points (e.g., Bayley Scales of Infant Development). Thus, for a test with a mean of 100 and a standard deviation of 15, a standard score of 85 would indicate that the child scored one standard deviation below the mean. If the child received a standard score of 70, then this also means that the child is performing two standard deviations below the mean (and would automatically qualify for services). See The Normal Curve diagram at the back of this book for a comparison of different scores.

## Calculating and Reporting the Age

Most clinicians report an infant or young child's age in years and months. It becomes more complicated when the days since birth are also considered. For example, if a child is 1 year, 2 months, 14 days, should you report the child as 1 year and 2 months, or 1 year and 3 months? A good way to avoid this potential confusion is to report the child's age in years, months, and days, as well.

When reporting the child's age, our preference is to use a dash, which distinguishes the months (12 in a year) from decimals (which are divisible by 10). Thus, we report a child as 1-2 when the child is 1 year, 2 months. Again, it's easy to avoid these issues by reporting the age as 1 year, 2 months. Some evaluators report the age in terms of months only. However, this leaves more work for the readers, who then have to calculate the years and months on their own.

Here are some examples of how to calculate a child's age.

Example 1

|  | Year | Month | Day |
|---|---|---|---|
| Date of Testing | 2002 | 12 | 21 |
| -Date of Birth | 2000 | 2 | 14 |
| Age | 2 | 10 | 7 |

Note that you work from right to left, calculating the days first, then months, then years. Thus, 21 – 14 is 7, 12 – 2 is 10, and 2002 – 2000 is 2. This is an easy example that does not require carrying any information from one column to another column. Consider an example in which carrying is required.

Example 2

|  | Year | Month | Day |
|---|---|---|---|
| Date of Testing | 2003 | 3 | 8 |
| -Date of Birth | 2001 | 9 | 28 |
| Age | 1 | 5 | 10 |

Here is how this was calculated:

|  | Year | Month | Day |
|---|---|---|---|
|  | 2002 | 14 |  |
|  |  | ~~3~~ | 38 |
| Date of Testing | ~~2003~~ | ~~3~~ | ~~8~~ |
| -Date of Birth | 2001 | 9 | 28 |
| Age | 1 | 5 | 10 |

The first calculation is days. You cannot have a negative result. Thus, you can't subtract 28 from 8. Borrow one month from the month column. Now you have 2 months instead of 3. In the days column, you have 30 days (you borrowed one month, or 30 days, from the month column), plus the 8 days, and so the total is 38. 38 − 28 = 10. Now go to the month column. You can't subtract 9 from 2. Thus, you need to go to the year column. Take one year and add this (or 12 months), to the month column. 12 + 2 = 14. Now you can perform 14 − 9 = 5. Finally 2002 − 2001 = 1.

## *Taking Prematurity Into Account When Calculating the Child's Age*

Make sure that you ask if the child was born premature and, if so, by how many weeks (or months). If the child was born premature, you need to determine if you should adjust the child's age for prematurity or not. (Sometimes the child is under the care of a foster parent, and it is not known if the child was born premature, as birth and early developmental information may not be known.) There is controversy about determining up to what age you should adjust for prematurity (Black & Matula, 2000). However, most authors agree that age should be adjusted for prematurity at least up to the age of 12 months. Then the test scoring, and the calculation of developmental delays, should be based on the age adjusted for prematurity, and not on the chronological age. Note if you adjust for prematurity in your report.

Normal gestational age is about 40 weeks. This means that a mother normally carries the growing fetus for about 40 weeks until birth. A child is considered premature if born at less than 38 weeks of gestational age. You can adjust the child's age downward for each day the child was premature. See the following examples.

A child is 12 months old. He was born at 32 weeks gestation (about 2 months premature). Rather than considering the child to be 12 months old, you would consider the child to have been born 2 months later than his actual birth date. His chronological age, adjusted for prematurity, would be 10 months old.

A child is 9 months old. He was born at 24 weeks gestation (yes, children are born this early). The child is considered to be 16 weeks premature, and thus the child's age adjusted for prematurity is about 5 months old.

When calculating chronological age and age adjusted for prematurity, it is recommended that you calculate based on the year, month, and days. Using the number of months alone is not sufficient when working with infants. For example, a child who is 5 months old and 25 days is almost 6 months old. When using tests you need to determine if that specific test indicates to round up or down.

## A Note About Pervasive Developmental Disorders and Autism

There are an increasing number of children being identified with autism or one of the pervasive developmental disorders. It is therefore important to be knowledgeable about these disorders. Please see chapter 9 on Identifying autism and pervasive developmental disorders for more information.

## Reasons for Developmental Delays and Disorders

Most of the children you see in the EIP have developmental delays for reasons that are not known. There are factors that are associated with children developing more slowly. However, when working with an individual child, it is not usually possible to determine the extent to which any single cause has had an impact on the child's development. Certainly an enriched environment which stimulates the child's cognitive development, communication, motor skills, adaptive skills, and social development is helpful. Keep in mind that many children from a stimulating environment may also have developmental delays. Thus, the impact of the environment on a given child is usually uncertain. Bilingualism also influences language development. Although children who are learning two languages may develop at a slightly slower pace initially, they usually catch up within a few years.

## *Determining Eligibility for Services Based on Physical and Mental Conditions with a High Probability of Developmental Delay*

Some physical and medical conditions will automatically qualify a child for Early Intervention services if they are diagnosed by a physician. The following is a list of conditions in New York State that allow a child to become eligible for EIP services regardless of whether or not they have a developmental delay. Check with your locality to determine which conditions qualify a child for intervention in your area.

Albinism
Angleman's
Aniridia
Arthrogryposis
Attention Deficit Disorder
Blindness
CHARGE Association
Cleft Palate
Conductive Hearing Loss
Congenital Hydrocephalus
Congenital Muscular Dystrophy
Cystic Periventricular
Leukomalacia
Dyspraxia Syndrome
Down Syndrome
Edward's Syndrome
Emotional Disturbance of
Childhood
Encephalocele
Fetal alcohol syndrome
Fragile X
Infantile Autism
Infantile Cerebral Palsy
Infantile Spasms with Intractable
Epilepsy
Infantile Spasms without
Intractable Epilepsy
Intraventricular Hemorrhage
Kernicterus
Low Birth Weight

Lobster Claw
Low Vision
Microcephalus
Mixed Conductive and
Sensorineural Hearing Loss
Multiple Anomalies of Brain
Optic Nerve Coloboma,
Acquired
Optic Nerve Coloboma,
Congenital
Other Myopathies
Patau's Syndrome
Pervasive Developmental
Disorder
Phocomelia
Prader-Willi
Prolonged Post Traumatic Stress
Disorder
Reduction Deformities of Brain
Retinopathy of Prematurity
Sensorineural Hearing Loss
Spina Bifida with Hydrocephalus
Spina Bifida without
Hydrocephalus
Spinal Cord Injury
Unspecified Anomalies of Ear
with Hearing Impairment
Visual Deprivation Nystagmus
Werdnig-Hoffman Syndrome

*III.*

# General Considerations When Conducting Early Intervention Evaluations

## The Three Major Aspects of the Evaluation Process

There are three important aspects of the early intervention evaluation: the parent interview, the formal assessment, and the informal assessment. These three parts of the evaluation are each necessary in order to create an accurate and comprehensive description of the child. The parent interview involves talking with the parent about the child's developmental history and present status, using both structured interviews as well as your own questions. The formal assessment involves using formal measures to compare the child's developmental level with same-age peers. The informal assessment is based on your observations of the child performing evaluation tasks, engaging in spontaneous play and interacting with others. Once the evaluation is complete, you will need to analyze all of your results, comparing and contrasting data from each part of the evaluation in order to develop a clear understanding of the child's functioning.

## Reasons for Referral to Early Intervention

*Motor Skills*. Developmental delays can be detected even in the first year of life. Infants—children under the age of 1—are often referred to Early Intervention for delays in their motor skills. For example, parents may notice that their child is not rolling over, not holding his head up, not grasping toys, or not sitting or standing on his own, as other children his age are doing. During routine visits, pediatricians commonly ask whether the child is achieving these motor milestones, and, if not, he should then be referred for an evaluation. Children are seen by a physical therapist and/or receive an occupational therapy evaluation to assess motor skills. Physical therapists assess children's musculoskeletal development, including muscle tone, range of movement, and spine and leg length. They also assess postural reactions and reflexes, and gross motor skills. Occupational therapists assess children's tone, range of motion, fine motor skills, perceptual motor development, sensory processing, and adaptive skills.

***Communication Skills***. For children from ages 1 to 3, one of the most common reasons for referral to EIP is concern about communication skills. Parents often complain that their child is not saying enough, is not responding to his name, or is not following directions. When children are referred to EIP for communication problems, they are seen by a speech pathologist, who assesses the child's expressive and receptive language, including syntax, semantics, pragmatics and phonology. The speech pathologist will also assess the quality and resonance of the voice, the fluency (rate and flow), and the articulation. The evaluator will look at oral-motor issues and feeding behavior. The parent will be interviewed regarding the history of the child's speech and language development. If the speech pathologist determines that the communication delays may be related to a disorder, such as autism or pervasive developmental disorder, then a psychological evaluation should be recommended.

***Behavioral and Emotional Issues***. As children reach the age of two, there are an increasing number of referrals for behavioral and emotional issues. Common concerns are, for example, "my child ignores me when I call him," "my child is overly active," or "my child is always hitting and pushing." When a child is seen in Early Intervention, the core evaluation will include a developmental evaluation, which assesses social-emotional functioning. If during the developmental evaluation a significant behavioral or emotional problem is detected, the child can be referred for a supplemental psychological evaluation. The psychologist will assess a variety of issues, including relatedness, hyperactivity, aggressive behavior, separation/attachment issues, anxiety, post-traumatic stress, and autism or pervasive developmental disorder.

**Daily Living Skills**. Children may also be seen in Early Intervention because of difficulties with daily living skills, such as eating or sleeping. These skills will be assessed in the core developmental or psychological evaluation and can be further assessed by an occupational therapist or speech evaluator (in the case of feeding difficulties).

**Cognitive Development**. Some children are referred for evaluations because their parents report that they don't know as much as expected for their age. The special educator or psychologist who conducts the developmental evaluation will assess general cognitive development and will refer for further evaluations if there are other areas of difficulty.

## Scheduling Appointments

The evaluator's first contact with the family is usually by phone, to set up the appointment for the evaluation. The appointment should be made as soon as possible after receiving the referral because of the 45-day time limit for completing the evaluation process. The evaluator is encouraged to use the *Sample Telephone Script for Scheduling Appointments*. This script has been developed through trial and error over hundreds of evaluations by the authors and other evaluators. Although each evaluator has his or her own style and way of communicating, we have found that following the script can be helpful in assuring that the important issues are addressed. See the explanation following the script for tips on how to avoid problems in your initial contact with the parent.

# Sample Telephone Script for Scheduling Appointments

### Initial greeting/purpose of call

"Hello, my name is _____, and I am calling from _____ Agency to speak with _____ to schedule the Early Intervention evaluation for _____ (child name)."
"Hello, this is Ms. _____."

### Pleasantries

"Hello, how are you?"
"Fine, thank you."

### Your discipline/evaluation & scheduling

"I am the _____ (your discipline), and I will be conducting the _____ (type of evaluation) of your child. Would you be available on _____ date/time for the evaluation?"
(Proceed to schedule the evaluation)

### Address verification

"What is your address?"

### Cross Streets

"Can you tell me the cross streets?"

### Alternate Phone Number

"Do you have any other phone number, work number, cell-phone or beeper number that I may have, just in case I can't reach you at this number on the day of the evaluation?"

### Verification/No go if no verification

"The day before the evaluation and about an hour before the evaluation I will call you to confirm the appointment. It is very important for me to do this to avoid any scheduling problems. If I cannot confirm with you then I will not go to your home, and we will have to reschedule the appointment."

### Approximate arrival times

"The appointment time I am giving you is approximate. I should arrive between the hours of _____ and _____. I will be traveling from another home, and the evaluation times vary. However, I will call you just before the appointment time to confirm the appointment and to try to give you a more specific arrival time."

### Session length

"The evaluation should take approximately an hour to an hour and a half to complete."

### Answer questions

"Do you have any questions?"

## *Rationale for Using the Sample Telephone Script for Scheduling Appointments*

### *Initial greeting/purpose of call*

"Hello, my name is _____, and I am calling from _____ Agency to speak with _____ to schedule the Early Intervention evaluation for _____ (child name)."

This is such a simple thing to do, and yet we have made mistakes with this simple introduction. We have found that if you mention the four points above (your name, your agency, who you wish to speak with, and the reason you are calling), you can avoid an awkward beginning to your call.

When you first call, the parent may not know or recall who was supposed to be calling, or know the difference between the Early Intervention Program, the evaluating agency, and the actual evaluator. This may need to be explained. In addition, it's normal for the parent to have mixed feelings about the evaluation. The parents may be looking forward to getting the evaluation results, so they can find out if their child has any delays or disabilities. Additionally, it is understandable that the parent may be anxious and/or concerned about the process and/or the outcome. It is natural for the parent to wonder who the evaluator is, what kind of background/expertise he/she has, and if he/she will complete an effective evaluation of the child. Approaching parents with a calm and reassuring tone can help them to feel more comfortable with you and your evaluation.

### *Pleasantries*

"Hello, how are you?"

Even though we ordinarily will exchange pleasantries with people we know, we sometimes don't do this in our professional role. This won't matter much for some parents. But other parents may perceive you as cold or uncaring if you don't exchange pleasantries and don't treat them personably. Looking at this another way, you can immediately help most parents feel a little more comfortable by being personable to the extent this feels right for you. It is good to be professional, but it is also good to be personal enough so that parents will feel comfortable with you as you go through the evaluation process.

### *Your discipline/evaluation & scheduling*

"I am the _____ (your discipline), and I will be conducting the _____ (type of evaluation) of your child. Would you be available on _____ date/time for the evaluation?"

Scheduling sounds like a simple task. It *can* be simple, but it sometimes takes a lot of time. We find that when parents take a long time to agree on a date, or have trouble committing to an evaluation time, this may indicate that they have very busy schedules. It may also indicate that they are anxious about the evaluation process, or may have mixed feelings about the evaluation. Try to be flexible with the parents' schedules and also address any concerns or anxieties they may have when you meet them.

### *Address verification*

"What is your address?"

This is another very simple task that can easily go wrong. We schedule hundreds of evaluations. However, we still find we make more address mistakes than we'd like. A simple thing like having the wrong address can add many minutes to your travel, costing you valuable time and arriving late to the appointment. We suggest asking the parent to state the address. Do not say "Do you live at 55 Maple Street, Apartment 2?" It is easy for a person to respond by saying yes. However, they may be half listening to the children playing in the next room and not paying full attention to you. We find that when the parent says their street address, child's name, or other information, that information is consistently more accurate than if you state the address and ask the parent to verify it.

## Cross Streets

"Can you tell me the cross streets?"

This helps you to find the exact location of the home. This alone can save you time, especially in cities with lots of one-way streets—which are sometimes crowded and slow moving.

## Alternate Phone Number

"Do you have any other phone number, work number, cell-phone or beeper number that I may have, just in case I can't reach you at this number on the day of the evaluation?"

We consistently find that an alternate number helps when the parent can't be contacted, and this helps avoid cancelled appointments. If the parent has no phone number, then they must contact you. We strongly recommend that you have a cell phone, so the parent can contact you for any reason and so you can call the parent when in the field for any reason.

## Verification/No go if no verification

"The day before the evaluation and about an hour before the evaluation, I will call you to confirm the appointment. It is very important for me to do this to avoid any scheduling problems. If I cannot confirm with you, then I will not go to your home and we will have to reschedule the appointment."

We can't emphasize enough how important it is to confirm appointments. If the appointment cannot be confirmed but you go to the home anyway, there is a high probability that the person will not be there, thus wasting the trip. Our rule is that we do not go to appointments if they are not confirmed. In our experience, we find that there are very few scheduling problems, or no shows, if this rule is followed.

## Approximate arrival times

"The appointment time I am giving you is approximate. I expect to arrive approximately between the hours of _____ and _____. I will be traveling to your home and visiting another child before I see you—so I cannot give you an exact arrival time. However, I will call you just before our appointment time to confirm the appointment and give you a more specific arrival time."

Some parents want to know exactly when the evaluator will arrive. You can make your appointments exact. However, this would mean that you have to allow for extra time during the day between appointments. We do not feel that this is reasonable. Most parents will understand the nature of your work when you explain it to them. However, some parents are much more concerned about your arrival time and may be upset if you are even five minutes late. If you emphasize that you will arrive *approximately* between the hours of X and Y, then you can help avoid a parent becoming annoyed if your arrival time is not exact. Most parents are quite understanding, as long as they know what to expect from the beginning.

### Session length
"The evaluation should take approximately an hour to an hour and a half to complete."

This helps clarify the length of the session, so the parent can plan her time. If you detect any hesitation when making the appointment, it is a good idea to ask her if this appointment time is a good one, or if there are any questions or issues. If there are any issues with the evaluation, it may be wise to deal with them at the beginning, so that way the parent is more relaxed and prepared for the evaluation.

### Answer questions
"Do you have any questions?"

Answer any questions the parent may have. Some questions, however, are better answered during the evaluation. The purpose of this call is mainly to schedule the appointment. If the call lasts more than five minutes, that could indicate that you are discussing issues that might be more appropriately dealt with during the evaluation. A long phone call may indicate that the parent is very anxious and is trying to calm herself by having questions answered. Use your judgment in deciding how much detail to go into. However, you can probably calm the parent more by deferring some questions that are child specific to the evaluation session. Most parents will understand that questions about their child can only be fully answered after the evaluation has been complete. General questions about the Early Intervention Program, or other general questions, can be answered briefly, or politely deferred to the child's service coordinator when appropriate. Contact the service coordinator or evaluation agency if there are specific concerns raised in this call that may be helpful for the other professional to know about. For example, the mother might mention that she is pregnant and expecting to deliver within the next three weeks. The other Early Intervention professionals will appreciate your calling them, so that they can be informed about this. Ideally, the service coordinator will relay important information like this to all evaluators.

## Scheduling Policies

Whatever scheduling policy you adopt must be clearly communicated to the parent. If you follow our suggested policy of not going to appointments unless they are confirmed, then you must tell the parent this when you schedule the appointment. Otherwise, they can become quite unhappy, and rightfully so, if you do not show up for an appointment. If you have to cancel or reschedule an appointment for any reason, we recommend a direct call to the parent, with as much advance notice as possible.

## Sick Child

Appointments are frequently canceled because of illness. This is an important reason to confirm the appointment on the morning of the evaluation. Even if you confirm with the parents on the day before, you may find out on the following day that the child has developed a cold or has gone to the hospital with an asthma attack. It is a good idea to ask the parent if the child is feeling well when making the final confirmation call. If a child has more than a sniffle, and is not well enough to perform optimally, then another appointment will be needed. In addition, some children seen through the Early Intervention Program have medical conditions. Sometimes these conditions are not identified until you visit the home and take a thorough history. These conditions may affect the child's ability to perform during the evaluation.

## Arriving at the Appointment Times

When you are doing a number of evaluations in one day, it may be difficult to arrive at an exact time at each home. That is why it is recommended that you provide a window of time (we recommend 2 hours) in which you will arrive at each home. This gives you some wiggle room if another evaluation lasts longer or shorter, or if your travel time increases or decreases significantly, compared to what you had planned.

## Parent Feelings About the Evaluation Process

Parents react in many different ways and experience a range of emotions when it comes to having their child evaluated. The following represents some typical parent reactions to the evaluation process, and suggested responses to each one:

**1) Parents are concerned**: Most often parents are concerned about their child's development. They may have initiated the referral process, or perhaps the child's pediatrician suggested the evaluation after hearing the parents' concerns about the child. In this case, the evaluator can be supportive toward the parents and should be sure to address the parents' areas of concern in the evaluation and recommendations.

**2) Parents are concerned about only one issue**: Parents may be concerned about only one area of development, even though there may be other areas of difficulty. For example, a parent may say, "I'm only concerned about my child's speech." However, the child may be delayed in other areas, or the child may demonstrate global developmental delays. In this case, although the evaluator should be supportive of the parent's initial concern, it is your obligation as a professional to inform her about all of your findings. If the evaluation is conducted successfully, and if the parents are engaged as partners in the evaluation process, then they should be much more open to accepting the evaluator's findings, even if they include areas of concern that the parents did not initially identify themselves. Work with the parents to educate them about your findings, and try to join them in an effort to help facilitate the child's development.

**3) Parents not concerned but agree to evaluation**: The parents may have no concerns about their child but may agree to the evaluation because of the recommendations of a pediatrician or other professional. For these parents, the evaluator can reinforce the benefits of having an evaluation and having a professional assessment of their child's development. The evaluator can also remind the parents that they can choose whether or not to accept the evaluation recommendations and whether or not they want services for their child.

**4) Parents angry about the referral**: In our experience, this kind of reaction is not common. However, because it presents a particular challenge to the evaluator, it helps to understand why parents react this way and to have different ways to respond. Some parents are angry about the evaluation out of fear, anxiety, or disappointment about their child's development. Maybe they cannot yet accept that their child is not developing as they had hoped. Some parents are angry because they really do not understand why professionals have recommended that their child be evaluated. They may feel that they must comply with the recommendations of the child's pediatrician, or another professional, in order to be viewed favorably by that professional. Sometimes, one parent wants the evaluation but another does not, and this may cause conflict within the family. Or perhaps the parents are under some legal pressure, such as when they have a matter pending in court, and are going along with the evaluation in order to avoid problems with the judge.

When parents have negative feelings about the referral process, they should be reminded that the EI program is voluntary. They should be reminded that, even if they give their consent to the evaluation, they can still choose whether or not to accept the recommendations. The evaluator can inform the parents about the benefits of the EI program. For example, if services are needed it is better to start them when the child is young—the earlier the better. If the parents refuse to give consent, then the evaluator must discontinue the evaluation process.

## Conducting Evaluations Individually or in a Team

Home-based evaluations can be conducted individually or in a team (or arena) format. There are possible advantages and disadvantages of each approach. In general, we have found there are significant advantages to performing evaluations in a team format. However, this is not always possible because of the challenges of scheduling evaluations with two or more professionals and the parents. If you only have experience conducting evaluations individually, you may want to see if you can arrange to perform some evaluations with other professionals to try out the team format, and see if this works for you.

Conducting evaluations individually means that each professional schedules and conducts his/her evaluation at a different time. This type of format allows an evaluator more flexibility in scheduling, as there is no need to coordinate schedules with anyone besides the parent. In addition, some children, such as shy or fearful children, may relate better to one evaluator at a time. Parents may also find it easier to establish rapport and may feel more comfortable in revealing personal information to one person. It may also be easier for the evaluator to focus and less potentially distracting to parent and child than if multiple evaluators are present.

The team format means that two or more evaluators meet with the child at the same time. Usually each evaluator will spend some time interacting directly with the child and parents while the other evaluators observe. Each evaluator will also obtain information that is relevant for his/her discipline. There are several advantages to team evaluations. First, the evaluator will gain additional information and insight by observing the child interacting with other professionals and by discussing the case as a team at the time of the evaluation. For example, a physical therapist might learn more about the child's family background by listening to the parent interview conducted by a social worker. A speech evaluator might learn more about the child's play skills by watching the child complete the tasks presented by a psychologist. Perhaps an occupational therapist might observe the child's adaptive skills when the child is working with the teacher. A second advantage to the team approach is that the entire evaluation process can be completed more quickly than with an individual format. Because fewer appointments are necessary, scheduling the evaluations is easier for both the families and the evaluation agency. Third, the evaluation can be engaging and enjoyable when working with other colleagues on a regular basis. Performing individual home-based evaluations can be isolating professionally, as there is little interaction with other professionals.

## *Performance Differences With Different Evaluators During a Team Evaluation*

During a team evaluation, if the child's behavior and performance is consistent with different evaluators, then all the evaluation reports should be consistent, thus strengthening the findings of the team. If the child's behavior was consistent, and the evaluators did not report in a similar way, then the team needs to spend more time reviewing their findings together prior to writing their reports. However, even when two or more evaluators see the child during the same session, the child may react differently to each evaluator. Could it be that the child did not react well with the first evaluator because the child had not yet warmed up to the testing situation? Or could it be that the child was tired and did not perform well for the last evaluator? Another hypothesis could be that the child preferred certain activities that one of the evaluators presented. Possible reasons for performance differences include the gender of the evaluator, personality of the evaluator, race of the evaluator, activity presented to the child, time of evaluation (beginning, middle, end of visit), and the child's physical state (hungry, tired). Explain any possible performance issues in your report.

In our experience, many children with developmental delays prefer manipulative tasks over verbal tasks. For example, a child may play well and be cooperative when given a peg to put in a pegboard. Yet, the same child may get annoyed, or even have a tantrum, if required to name pictures of familiar objects. This may occur during a team evaluation when one evaluator conducting a developmental evaluation uses many manipulative toys and another evaluator, for example, a speech therapist, does many verbal tasks. In this case the differences in the child's performance can be attributed to the child's preference for manipulative tasks over ones that involve language. Possibly the child is delayed in language and therefore prefers to avoid language–based tasks. This is useful information to include in the reports and summaries, and can help inform the recommendations for treatment. Simple statements can help clear up a lot of confusion at the IFSP meeting, such as, "The child seemed to be much more cooperative when engaged in manipulative tasks over verbal ones." Another statement might be, "This child seems to enjoy playing with objects and toys and becomes frustrated when asked to name or point to objects." Finally, an interpretative comment may be needed. For example, "This child seems to have difficulty responding to verbal requests because of his difficulty understanding the requests."

## Performance Differences
## On Different Individual Evaluations

When a child is evaluated on several different occasions, his behavior might be similar or different on each occasion. When the child's behavior is consistent over time, the results are usually strengthened. For example, a child may be relaxed and cooperative with all evaluators. This suggests that the child is generally relaxed and cooperative. Of course, this hypothesis must always be checked with the parent.

Sometimes a child may present differently with each evaluator on different visits. Many factors could account for this, and an effective evaluation report will try to determine the reasons for these differences. They may be due to differences in the evaluator's presentations and the types of evaluations they are doing. They may also be related to differences in how the child is feeling at the times of the visits. The important question becomes: "Which parts of each evaluation reveal this child's typical functioning?" To help address this issue, ask the parent if the child's performance and behavior was optimal or typical. If the child's behavior was not typical on a particular day, you must attempt to understand why by discussing this with the parent and by documenting this in the report.

*IV.*

# Beginning the Evaluation

## The First Steps

The evaluation process begins as soon as you make the first contact with the family. By being more aware of the issues that arise when you first arrive at the home and meet the family, you will be better prepared to get the evaluation off to a good start. A willingness to learn about and understand the culture of the family will also help you to gain the family's respect and trust. In this chapter we will present the issues we have faced early on in the evaluation process, and we will describe what procedures have worked best for us.

## Safety

Home-based evaluators in the EIP become accustomed to going to a different home, in a different neighborhood, for each evaluation. While this can be a rewarding and interesting experience, it can also present some safety issues. To make the evaluation process a safe and comfortable one, we recommend that you take certain precautions. If you have concerns about a particular home or neighborhood prior to the evaluation, you can plan to do the evaluation in a team format with a colleague. If you arrive at a home and feel unsafe, then you can call the family and ask to be met outside and escorted into the home or apartment. If you feel that this is insufficient, then you may need to cancel the appointment and return another day with a colleague. When entering an unfamiliar home, avoid poorly lit stairways and check elevators before entering. We recommend that you take elevators and avoid stairs when possible. This can help avoid slips and falls. Any specific safety concerns should be reported to the evaluation agency so that other evaluators can be informed. The service coordinator also should be notified, so that these issues can be addressed with the family, particularly if they affect the child's living situation. These issues also may affect whether the services can be delivered in the home.

## Initial Contact with the Family

*First Impressions*. Within the first minutes after meeting you, the family will form their first impressions of you and the evaluation experience. It is normal for the family to feel a bit nervous about the evaluation process. Even if the parents already believe that their child has some areas of difficulty, they may still feel upset when they hear this news delivered by a professional. Do whatever you can, starting as soon as you enter the home, to help the family feel at ease.

*Introductions*. One way to help the parents feel at ease is to immediately tell them your name, your discipline, the name of the evaluation agency, and the kind of evaluation you are going to perform.

*Shaking Hands*. Most families will appreciate it if you greet them by shaking their hands. Doing something as simple as shaking hands sends a message that you feel comfortable with the family. Not shaking their hands can be interpreted negatively, perhaps that you do not feel comfortable with the family or the situation. Although many families will appreciate your shaking hands, there are families in which this is not appropriate or not consistent with their traditions. For example, some families have religious traditions which forbid any physical contact, including shaking hands, between a married woman and any man besides her husband. You may not be able to predict which families have these traditions, so offer your hand and let them inform you if this is not appropriate in their culture.

*Finding a Good Location and Place to Sit*. A respectful approach is to ask a parent first where they would like you to sit. Sometimes they will give you a choice, or ask you where you would like to conduct the evaluation. Look for a spacious area where the child can sit comfortably with you on the floor. If a living room is available, it can often work well for the parent interview and for your work with the child. The child's bedroom or a playroom may also be suitable; however, if there are too many toys around, it can be distracting for the child. In addition, try to choose a place to work where you will not get in the way of other family members.

**Sense of Humor**. Families usually appreciate it if you have a sense of humor. It is hard to work with babies and toddlers without being spontaneous and willing to expect the unexpected. One toddler might sit on your lap or take a box of tissues out of your bag; another might jump up and down in excitement or cry when you pack up to leave. You can put a family at ease by showing them that you are experienced with young children, and that you are comfortable with whatever their child presents. If you can relax and laugh at humorous situations, the family usually relaxes as well.

**Approaching the Child**. Your approach to each child will need to be tailored to his individual needs. Different interpersonal approaches work with different children. However, most children seem to respond well when you approach them slowly and carefully. You may want to greet and acknowledge the child when you first arrive. However, it is usually better to wait a while before physically approaching the child. Children usually warm up more easily once they see that the evaluator has established rapport with their parents. Some children will approach the evaluator on their own once they see that the evaluator has connected with their parents. Other children may take time to warm up.

**Touching the Child**. When working with young children, you are often confronted with displays of physical affection as well as aggressive behavior. The way you respond to this, and the way you interact physically with the child, will impact on the entire evaluation process. Try to be sensitive to the child and respond in a way that helps you establish a trusting relationship with him. If the child is affectionate, you may want to respond in a variety of ways, such as talking to him, patting his head, or picking him up. Take notice if the child is overly affectionate or overly aggressive. Ask the parent if this behavior is typical with strangers. If the child is aggressive, you may need to set limits in a way that helps the child to refocus but is not punitive. Be sure to be sensitive to the parents' position in your interactions. Parents may feel very comfortable about your being close to their child, or they may feel uncomfortable. Sometimes the parents may ask the child to give you a hug or a kiss goodbye. We suggest that you respond in a way that is

63

comfortable for you and also sensitive to the child and parent. When working with young children, use your judgment as to when physical contact is appropriate. It is usually best to refrain from much physical contact with the child unless the child seems to need comforting or initiates the contact himself. Also note if the child seeks comfort from you, a stranger, or from the parent.

***Family Configurations***. In your work as a home-based evaluator you will be confronted with many different family configurations. There are single-parent households, dual-parent households, children with siblings and without siblings, children in foster families, children raised by aunts and uncles or grandparents, and children living with or without extended family. In our experience with many immigrant families in New York, there may be several families living in one apartment with several bedrooms, and no living room or dining room. In these cases, the evaluation may have to take place in the bedroom. There may be other relatives participating in the evaluation or moving about the home. In order to show respect for the family and to get as clear a picture of the child as possible, you should try to meet and acknowledge the relatives and you should be flexible in obtaining information about the child from the different people present, with the permission of the parents, when appropriate. Sometimes the parent who attends the evaluation appointment does not spend the most time with the child. For example, the grandmother may be the primary caretaker and babysitter during the day and may have more information about the child's skills and daily routines than the parent. In this case it would be important to include the grandmother in the interview, if possible.

***Different Impressions of the Child***. Sometimes there are two parents or family members with quite different impressions of the child's functioning. For example, take the case of a family in which the father is working full-time and the mother is a full-time homemaker. Perhaps the father spends less time with his child, but has strong feelings about his child's functioning. Perhaps he is less aware of his child's developmental difficulties, and the mother may have first identified the child as having possible developmental delays. You will avoid unnecessary conflict if you respectfully elicit input from both parents and try to reach an understanding with them about the child's functioning at the time of the evaluation. When differences of opinion cannot be reconciled, acknowledge the differences, and attempt to address them in your report. Your role is to understand their perspectives. Your role is not to provide family counseling or to help them reconcile possibly longstanding differences.

## Culture of the Family

From the moment you enter the home to perform an evaluation, you are confronted with different aspects of the family's cultural background. You may notice a flag from the family's country of origin, religious articles, or religious shrines. Some families display artwork reflecting their customs and beliefs or photos of their relatives and their travels. When working with families you need to be aware of your environment, as it helps you understand the culture of the family.

The culture of the family may reflect aspects of their country of origin, but may also be related to the family's level of acculturation, immigration status, religion, language, customs, traditions, the age of the family members, and other factors. Let's say you are visiting a family from Mexico, for example. The fact that they are from Mexico does not give you that much information. You need to ask for more specific information. For example, which state in Mexico they are from? Are they from the capital of that state, or from a small rural village? Did family members in Mexico own a business, or were they farmers? Did they have a high income and many opportunities in their country, or are they a poor family that has emigrated to find a better life? It is also important to look at their current living situation. Do they live surrounded by many families from their country of origin, or do they live in a neighborhood with families from other countries? It is important to be aware of as many aspects of the family's culture as possible. You can refer to a number of resources for information in this area (Garcia, Coll, & Magnuson, 2000; Lynch & Hanson, 1998; McGoldrick, Giordano & Pearce, 1996; Padilla, 1992). The more you understand the culture of the family, the better position you will be in to assess the child's skills and development. The following are some examples of family/cultural issues you may encounter while working in Early Intervention.

**Clothing**. You need to determine what you feel comfortable wearing to conduct an evaluation. Playing with children on the floor requires informal clothing. However, many families expect professionals to dress in a professional manner. Some families will give more respect to a professional who looks more mature and is more formally dressed. Evaluators should consider these issues when choosing what to wear and keep in mind that the parents may perceive you differently based on your appearance. Some families have a custom of taking off their shoes when they enter the home. It helps to notice or to ask if this is the custom and to offer to take your shoes off. Even if the family informs you that it is fine to leave your shoes on, they will appreciate that you were considerate about their preferences.

Family members may dress themselves or their children in different ways for the evaluation. Some dress up in a more formal manner, others wear comfortable clothes. Occasionally, when the evaluation is conducted in the home, family members may even be as informal as to wear bathrobes and slippers. The important issue is not to make assumptions based on the family's appearance without being well informed. Sometimes, there are reasons why a family member is dressed a certain way. For example, one mother we saw was resting on the couch wearing pajamas when we arrived. Only after talking with her did we find out that she had recently returned home from the hospital after back surgery.

**Time**. Families have different concepts of time, which may be related to their cultural background or to their personal habits. This is often evident when scheduling evaluation appointments. For example, some families are surprised when the evaluator arrives at the scheduled time of the appointment. They may be in the middle of feeding or bathing the child. Sometimes the child is asleep. This can be frustrating if you are trying to keep to your own schedule of evaluation appointments. Nevertheless, try to be as flexible as you can while encouraging the parent to begin the evaluation process. If you come across as being annoyed or in a rush, this will hurt your ability to establish rapport with the family and complete the evaluation effectively. It also may help to give all of your families a range of time within which you are expected to arrive (e.g., "I should arrive at your house between 1 and 3 pm").

***Food and Drink***. Some families offer the evaluator food and drink as a measure of hospitality. You can accept or respectfully decline, depending on what feels most comfortable for you. Keep in mind the importance of this generosity from the family. If you decline, do so respectfully—most families will understand. However, if the family feels that your refusal represents a lack of respect, then this may interfere with their ability to trust you, relate to you, and complete the evaluation process.

***Child-Rearing Practices***. Families may engage in a variety of different childrearing practices. For example, some families we see in Early Intervention allow their children to use the bottle or the pacifier until the age of five. Other families allow their children to continue breastfeeding until they naturally wean themselves. Some parents allow their children to sleep with them and others do not. Some families begin toilet training when the child is age one; others wait until the child is closer to age three and shows interest on his own. Keep these factors in mind when assessing a child's adaptive functioning. Sometimes what appears to be a developmental lag may only represent a different child-rearing style. Ask questions about child-rearing practices, so they can be understood more fully.

## Consent

Before beginning the evaluation, the parent/caregiver must sign a consent form, which gives you permission to conduct the evaluation. Allow the parent the opportunity to read the forms. Put the parent at ease by explaining that her signature on the consent forms only allows the evaluations to be conducted—it does not mean that she must accept the evaluator's recommendations. It does not take away any parental rights. In addition, let the parent know that she can withdraw from the evaluation process at any point.

## Using a Translator

If you do not speak the language of the child you are evaluating, you will need to work with a translator. The translator may be another professional or a family member. Before you begin working with the translator, you will want ask a few important questions. For example, how knowledgeable is the translator of the child's dominant language? How fluent is the translator in English—how much does the translator understand? Has this person ever served as a translator before? It is important to know these things, so that you can assess the accuracy of the information you receive from the translator. In addition, you will need to give clear instructions as to how to conduct the translation. It is best to tell the translator to translate exactly what you say without adding any additional comments. That way, the child will receive accurate instructions on how to proceed with evaluation tasks. In addition, ask the translator to translate what the child says as closely to "word for word" as possible. (Keep in mind, however, that two or three words in one language might translate as only one word in another language.) If you notice that the translator gets involved in a conversation with the child, or with the adult, ask the translator to inform you of what was said. Keep in mind that the use of a translator will alter the test administration and will likely alter the results. Only by working closely with the translator will you gain a better understanding of how much the child understands, how much the child is able to respond to requests, and the nature of the use of the child's language. For further suggestions on working with a translator, see Lynch (1998).

## Using A Computer

We strongly recommend using a laptop computer to gather information elicited during the parent interview. You will need to be a good typist to be able to gather the information quickly.

There are several advantages to using a laptop computer. First, you can get more accurate information this way, as compared with using a paper and pencil to take notes. If you are an adequate typist, you can type much of the important information gathered from the parent as the parent is speaking. That way, you do not have to recreate the session hours later when you may have forgotten some important details. If desired, you may even jot down a quote from the parent. Second, using a laptop is efficient. It allows you to take notes directly. The alternative is writing down notes on paper once during the evaluation session, and then copying your notes into a computer when returning to your office. This can take up a lot of extra time. Third, writing down notes on a laptop computer sends a message to the families that what they are reporting to you is very important. Fourth, if you write down your behavioral observations of the child at the end of the evaluation, as we recommend, this will lengthen your evaluation session. This is helpful, as it gives you more time to observe the child and gather information. Some professionals ask us if parents complain about the laptops, or if it interferes with the evaluation process. In our experience, in fact, very few families are concerned about the use of laptops. It seems that we have arrived at a time in which computers are widely accepted. We find that even many poor families have their own computers and Internet access. As long as you make an effort to make eye contact and establish rapport with the family, the laptop can be a very useful tool, making your work more efficient and helping to generate a more accurate and full reporting of the child.

## Explaining the Evaluation Process

Before beginning the evaluation, it is helpful to find out if previous evaluations have already been completed. If the parents are confused about the evaluation process, clarify the process as much as possible. Explain which evaluations are going to be scheduled. At the end of the evaluation, you can tell the parents what will happen when all the evaluations are completed. Explain that they should expect to receive evaluation reports and summaries prior to the IFSP meeting, and that they can speak with the initial service coordinator at any time regarding any questions about the process. It is also helpful to explain that any information given during the evaluation can be included in the report.

The parents will also need to know about the areas of development to be assessed that day. It helps if you explain how the evaluation will proceed. Typically, the parent interview is conducted first, followed by the formal evaluation. The evaluator may say to the parent, for example, "First I would like to speak with you to find out about your child's development, and then I will sit on the floor and work with your child." By explaining the process during the session, the parent knows what to expect and can relax more and follow your lead. Sometimes parents immediately tell their child to stop what they are doing and to come and sit down with the evaluator. In response to this sudden disruption, the child may start to cry. Tell the parents that you need to speak with them first and that the child can continue playing until you are ready to begin working with the child.

## Establishing Rapport with the Parents and Child

When you begin the evaluation, it helps to first concentrate on establishing rapport with the parents. This involves listening carefully to the parents' concerns about their child's development. It also involves being empathic when they express feelings or describe conflicts.

During the initial contact with the family, you can assess the child's readiness to participate in the evaluation and try to help the child adjust to the testing situation. If the child appears relaxed and comfortable and gradually warms up to you, the evaluation may proceed as planned. This usually means that you will interview the parent first and then sit down to work with the child. If, however, the child appears overexcited and restless, you may want to work with the child sooner and interview the parent later. When working with an overactive child, you will want to move through the evaluation items at a quicker pace. If the child appears very shy and fearful, begin by talking with the parent to allow the child time to warm up to you. In this case you may also want to make extra efforts to involve the parent in the formal evaluation. For example, you can encourage the parent to sit down on the floor with the child. A shy child will also be more responsive if he is given ample time to explore the evaluation materials before beginning specific evaluation tasks.

## *Sequence of the Evaluation*

Once you have passed the introductions and found a good spot to sit, you can begin the parent interview. There are advantages to speaking with the parents first. In general, parents are likely to be more comfortable allowing you to work with their children if they have an opportunity to speak with you first. This also gives the child time to warm up to you and the situation. If the parent interview takes place first, the active child has a chance to settle down, and the shy child has a chance to warm up. If the child is overly active, or if at any time you feel the child can't wait, then feel free to work with the child, and then return to the parent interview. However, once you have finished working formally with the child, most parents will want immediate feedback— "how did he do?" If you conduct the parent interview first, have the child engage in play, and then finish with the formal testing, you will be ready to give feedback after the formal testing is finished.

# V

# The Parent Interview

## Parent and Evaluator Collaboration

The parent interview works best when it is a joint process of discovery in which the evaluator and parent work together to try to understand the child (Hirshberg, 1996). The parent is an expert on her child—she has a history with him and has observed him in many situations over time. However, the evaluator is also an expert, in working with children from different backgrounds and with different developmental delays and disabilities. The evaluator also has education and training in early childhood development. For these reasons, both the parent and evaluator must work together, each contributing their expertise, in an effort to arrive at a full and balanced view of the child and his unique character, strengths, and needs. When the parent feels that she is an equal partner in the evaluation process, the evaluator is much more likely to complete the process successfully. If the evaluator describes the child in the report in a way that reflects this joint process, there is a better chance that the parent will embrace the report and the recommendations.

## Interviewing Technique

We have found that interviewing technique makes all the difference between obtaining optimal information and obtaining incomplete—or worse, incorrect—information about the child. Your technique is especially important when working with parents who say, "He's just a normal child." It is naturally very difficult for parents to accept that there is something "wrong" with their child. They may underestimate the extent of certain problems in order to see their child as "normal." They may say their child has difficulty in only one area when problems are apparent in other areas as well. While you want to be sure to address the parents' concerns, as a professional it is also your obligation to provide a complete evaluation and to give the parents your professional opinion.

## Assumptions

The more you are aware of the assumptions you bring with you to the evaluation, the better. All of us have assumptions and biases based on our experiences in life. It's impossible to get rid of all of our assumptions about others. However, we can become aware of our assumptions and work hard to test them when we are meeting someone new. One way to tell if you are using assumptions in your interviews with parents is to be aware if you are asking questions that end in, "right?" For example, would you say to a parent, "Your son is toilet-trained, right?" This may suggest to the parent that a child his age *should* be toilet trained. If, however, the child is not toilet-trained, the parent may become anxious. If you ask a mother about her employment history, do you say, "You're not employed, right?" Or do you ask, "Are you presently employed?" The differences may seem subtle, but they could communicate to the parent that you have a negative bias toward her and her child.

Another example of the danger of making assumptions comes from one of our experiences performing an evaluation in the South Bronx in New York City. The neighborhood and the building in which this family lived were particularly run down. Noticing the impoverished conditions, the evaluator assumed that the mother was receiving public assistance and was at home caring for her children. The evaluator therefore asked, "Are you at home full time?"—expecting the mother to say "yes." Instead, the mother responded that she had been working for many years in social services, was completing her bachelor's degree with a straight A average, and was planning to go to law school to further her work for civil rights. Even those of us with years of experience and clinical training fall into the assumptions trap. If you work hard to avoid this, you will communicate more effectively with families, and your evaluation will proceed more easily.

## Questioning Style

Your questioning style can make the difference between getting the right or the wrong information from parents. For example, you may have had the following experience: You go to a new doctor's office and are interviewed about your health. You are asked whether you have a series of medical conditions. After being asked a few questions, you begin to anticipate the doctor's next question and immediately say "no" when another medical condition is stated. You might even say "no" in response to a condition that you have, because you are so used to saying "no." The same pattern of response can happen when we work with parents. Be aware of this and do not ask too many yes/no questions. If you do, the parent might get used to responding in a set way. Instead, ask your questions in a way that helps the parent to think before responding. Keep in mind that the best results are obtained by engaging in a discussion with the parent about the child, rather than only going through a set list of questions. Also consider that there are times when you will want to use different questioning styles. Sometimes it is best to ask a yes/no question; at other times, it is more sensible to ask a general, open-ended question.

***Yes/No Questions***. Think of the following example. If you ask a parent, "Did your child reach his/her developmental milestones on time?" the parent could answer "yes" without giving information regarding the timing of specific milestones. This response, which fails to describe specific milestones, gives you very little information about the child's development. By asking this yes/no question, you are also putting the parent in the position of determining what it means to say "on time." Some parents may think a child should walk at 10 months; some may think 14 months is typical. It is more helpful when the professional who knows about the normal range of development determines whether that milestone is "on time" or "delayed." Here is another example: If you ask the parent, "Do you have any concerns about your child's developmental milestones?" the parent could say "no" without having to think about specific aspects of the child's development. Yet, if you ask, "When did your child walk?" you help the parent think more specifically about the child's skills. Sometimes parents may feel embarrassed that they do not recall certain information about their child.

Remembering when a child began to walk is usually easier to remember than other milestones, because people tend to ask about this in conversation. Remembering when a child sat up unsupported or said his first word may be more difficult. It is important to assure parents that they are not expected to remember all of the details, but what they do remember will be helpful in giving you a more complete picture of the child.

*General vs. Specific Questions*. There are times when it is more appropriate to ask general questions and times when it is better to ask specific questions. Be aware of the pros and cons of each and then plan accordingly. Here is another example of how a poor questioning technique can lead to incomplete information, this time in reference to social and emotional development. It is fine to ask a parent "Are you concerned about your child's behavior?" However, a typical response to this question is "No, I don't have any concerns; he's a normal child." If you do not ask specific questions at this point, you may conclude that there are no behavioral problems. However, this is an area in which you will want to ask for the parents' general impressions but then follow up by asking them about specific behaviors. For example, you may want to ask specific questions such as "How often does your child cry or have a tantrum?" Another specific question might be "When, in what situations, and for how long does your child cry?"

*How Questions*. How questions can elicit descriptive information about the child. For example, you might ask the parents the following: "How does your child act when frustrated?" "How does your child react when denied something?" "How does your child play with other children?" These questions are good for getting the parents to freely describe their child. Sometimes they may need additional, more specific questions to help them give more detailed information.

*Use of Examples*. Sometimes, in order to understand their descriptions more fully, you may want to ask parents to give you an example of their child's behavior. For instance, when asking about a child's frustration tolerance, you may ask, "When your child wants candy from a store, and you say 'no,' what does he do?" Alternatively, you may ask, "Can you give me an example of how you're child reacts when you say 'no'?"

***Paraphrasing***. Use paraphrasing when you want to see if you clearly understood what the parent reported. For example, you might ask, "So, your child has tantrums about four times per day, usually when you are outside or in a store, and you tell him 'no'?" This clarification helps you to understand the parents' observations before writing your report. Sometimes even minor mistakes can leave the parent feeling that you were not listening enough, did not take the time to get the details correct, or worse, that you were sloppy or unprofessional.

***Summarizing***. When you get to a natural pause in your interview, you may want to summarize what the parent has said. Paraphrasing usually refers to repeating back a small part of what was said to you. Summarizing is like paraphrasing, but it involves repeating a number of the most important elements of what you heard. For example, you might say, "So, if I hear you correctly, you are saying that your child is fairly well behaved, social, affectionate, and playful, but if you say 'no' he will have a tantrum briefly, perhaps once or twice a day. Is that right?" Check with the parents to see if you are correct. Allow them the opportunity to say that you got it right, partially correct, or wrong. Then you can continue until you do get it 100 percent right.

***Interpreting***. Interpreting is probably the most underutilized interviewing technique. In our experience, most interviewers ask their questions, conclude the interview and assessment, and then leave the parent with the understanding that they will provide feedback in the written report. While we don't suggest giving extensive feedback during the home visit, it can be helpful to make some simple interpretations as a way to open up communication with the parent. For example, a mother describes her child's significant behavior difficulties (multiple, daily tantrums, long crying episodes, and aggressive behavior) and begins to get tearful as she speaks. It may be helpful to say, "It sounds like this is pretty upsetting for you." If you are on track, this mother will likely feel understood, will respond affirmatively, and as a result may be more willing to speak openly about her experiences with her child.

## Assessing Behaviors and Interactions Fully

During the interviewing process it is very important that you gather detailed information about the child's behavior in order to understand the child to the fullest extent. This is especially true when describing the child's social skills, temperament, and emotionality. Assessing the child's behavior has five important components: defining the behavior, frequency, duration, intensity, and context. Consider asking the parent about a child's tantrums for example.

*Defining the Behavior*. Even very simple behaviors can be misunderstood. While we might all agree on what crying means, what we mean by a tantrum is much harder to define. To some parents, a tantrum may involve the child clenching his fist. Other parents may think of a tantrum as the child throwing himself down on the floor and kicking and screaming so loud that the neighbors call the Child Protective Services hotline. Be sure you understand what the parents mean when they say that the child tantrums by getting a detailed description of the child's behavior.

*Frequency*. It is not enough to ask a parent if her child frequently has tantrums. It is also important to find out how often the child has them. If the behavior occurs less than once a day, then ask if the child has tantrums once a week, twice a week, and so on. Some parents will respond that they are not sure or never counted. Tell them its fine to estimate.

*Duration*. Find out how long the tantrums last. It is one thing if a 2-year-old has tantrums for a minute at a time. Yet, it is something else if the child has tantrums for an hour while hitting and kicking on the floor and does not respond to attempts to soothe him.

*Intensity*. A child may cry softly or very loudly. A child may have a tantrum by crying and clenching his hands, or may have tantrums so severe that he bangs his head against the floor. Ask about the exact behaviors the child displays during the tantrum, and how intense they are.

**Context**. Behaviors do not have much meaning if the context is unclear. To understand a child's tantrums, it is much more helpful to know when and why they occur. Ask the parent to describe a typical instance when the child had a tantrum, so that you can understand the reasons for the behavior. Let's say that a mother reports that she is separated from her child's father, and that her son has tantrums once a week. Furthermore, she says that the tantrums only happen when her child's father leaves after a visit. Another mother reports that her child has tantrums whenever he is denied a piece of candy. These are two very different presentations, and the contexts should be described clearly in your report.

## Suggested Outline for Parent Interview

### PARENTS' CONCERNS, PRIORITIES AND RESOURCES
Concerns
Priorities
Resources

### FAMILY HISTORY
Living situation
Family configuration
Family immigration history
Language Issues
Parents educational background
Parents employment status
Involvement in early childhood programs or child care
Child's experience with social service agencies
Family history of developmental disabilities
History of domestic violence
History of drug or alcohol abuse
History of psychiatric illness

### DEVELOPMENTAL HISTORY
Pregnancy
Birth history
Early developmental milestones
Medical history
Medication
Surgeries
Hospitalizations
Allergies
Vision
Hearing

### DEVELOPMENTAL STATUS
Cognitive functioning
Communication
Daily living skills/adaptive behavior
Social emotional functioning
Motor Skills

### CLOSING DISCUSSION WITH PARENTS

# The Complete Parent Interview

## PARENTS' CONCERNS, PRIORITIES AND RESOURCES

### Concerns

Ask about all the parents' concerns regarding their child. One parent might only be concerned about the child's speech development. Another parent may have concerns about the child's speech, behavior, and motor development. Be sure to include all of the concerns.

### Priorities

Of all of the concerns mentioned by the parents, find out if there is one main concern that is a priority above the others. This should be a focus of your findings and recommendations. Other professionals will need to address this when developing an intervention plan at the Interdisciplinary Family Service Planning meeting (IFSP).

### Resources

In this section, outline the resources available to the parents, including financial resources, transportation and social support. The EI program supports families, and this information will be useful in developing a plan and communicating the family needs to the clinicians providing intervention services. Is this a family with a network of supportive and helpful friends, sufficient financial resources, and a car of their own? Will services need to be provided in the home? Is this a family with significant financial needs, few friends, no extended family, and no car?

## FAMILY HISTORY

### Living situation

Learn about the child's living situation. Some families in Early Intervention have four-bedroom homes in which there are two parents and two children. Other families of four live in one bedroom of a four-bedroom apartment, which they share with other families. While it is certainly better not to live in crowded conditions, we may automatically think that the first family is better off in all areas than the second one. However, further questioning will help us understand the relationship of the child's living situation to the child's other needs. What if, for example, the four-person family in the four-bedroom home includes two parents who work long hours, one older child in school and one younger child (the child being evaluated) who is cared for by an elderly babysitter who cannot go outside? By contrast, the young child in the other family has less space to play but perhaps many cousins to play with. Thus, it is best to learn about the uniqueness of each family without making assumptions.

### Family configuration

In addition to family members living in the home, there may be other important family members who do not live with the family. They may be involved with the family or not. If there is a non-custodial parent, find out if this parent visits, how often, and the relationship of the child to this parent. If the child lives in a foster family, indicate when the child was placed in foster care, the relationship of the child to the foster and biological families, the amount of visitation with the biological parents, and future plans for the child. This information can help you understand the child's social-emotional status.

### Family immigration history

Questions about where the parents were born, and if and when they immigrated to the U.S., will help provide information about their culture, their resources, and their understanding of U.S. policies and laws. Keep in mind that some families move to the U.S. to stay, others return to their country of origin and come back again. If they have lived outside the U.S. for an extended period of time, find out where and for how long.

### Language issues

It is extremely important to know the child's dominant language, as this is the language that must be used during the evaluation. In addition, it is important to know the languages spoken by family members and other important individuals in the child's life. Often children are exposed to multiple languages in their family, and this will impact on their evaluation performance. It is not sufficient to ask the parents about their language use. You should also ask about languages the child hears from others, such as babysitters, day-care providers, and siblings. Sometimes the parents only speak their native language, but the child is exposed mostly to English in a day-care setting.

### Parents' educational background

Questions about the parents' education may or may not be relevant to your work. Use your judgment as to whether this information is helpful for your evaluation.

### Parents' employment status

It is helpful to know if a parent is working, the hours they work, and the kind of work they do. This will help inform the other professionals who attend the IFSP meeting when they develop a plan of services for the child.

### Involvement in early childhood programs or child care

The objective here is not only to find out if the child is in day care and for how long each day. It is also helpful to know if the parent is content with this arrangement, if the parent wants more hours or a different kind of setting, and if the parent perceives any problems with the setting or the child's reaction to it. Remember that day care is not the only kind of early childhood activity to ask about. The child might attend music classes, activity classes, a library program, or a "mommy and me" program that might meet only once or twice a week for about 45 minutes. Again, find out how the child reacts to these experiences. This will help give you a clearer understanding of his socialization skills and how he relates to others.

### Child's experience with social-service agencies

If a child has been in foster care find out the name and contact information of the caseworker, the caseworker's supervisor, and if the current caretaker or parent has any information about the child's experiences there.

### Family history of developmental disabilities

Sometimes a family member, such as the parent or a sibling, has been diagnosed with a developmental disability and may have received early intervention, special education, or other developmental services. This will influence how the family reacts to the prospect of this child receiving Early Intervention services. This is a useful area to explore in order to understand the parents' thoughts and feelings about services for children with developmental disabilities.

### History of domestic violence

In our experience, few early intervention professionals have training in the area of domestic violence, and many are uncomfortable asking about this difficult area. Others may ask why there is a need to inquire about this area and, if a parent says that there is a history of domestic violence, what they should do with this information. We recommend considering this as an area of standard inquiry. Why? Domestic violence usually has a powerful effect on the lives of children, and the child you evaluate may be affected significantly by these events, even if he is not himself physically abused. Just witnessing or hearing excessive family conflict can be very disturbing or traumatizing to a young child. If you are given information about current domestic violence and possible risks to the child, we recommend consulting a supervisor, trusted colleague, or other Early Intervention professional involved with this child to make an appropriate plan. See the child abuse reporting rules for your state.

### History of drug or alcohol abuse

A history of parental drug or alcohol abuse may mean that the parent was involved with substance abuse in the past, or it could mean that the parent is currently abusing drugs or alcohol. We strongly recommend that you ask about these issues. If the parents are presently abusing drugs or alcohol, the child's welfare could be endangered and a plan must be developed to address this.

### History of psychiatric illness

Sometimes a parent has a significant history of psychiatric involvement. Again, this can be a difficult issue to discuss with the parent.

However, in our experience, many parents who have a history of psychiatric illness are comfortable sharing this and understand that it is something that needs to be addressed for the health and welfare of the parent and child.

## DEVELOPMENTAL HISTORY

### Pregnancy

Ask about whether the mother had any difficulties or medical complications during her pregnancy, which might have affected the infant's health. For example, was she placed on bed rest or on any special diets? Was she hospitalized during the pregnancy? Did she take any medications while pregnant? Learning about whether the mother received prenatal care can give you a sense of the mother's health and state of mind during the pregnancy. A good question to ask is when prenatal care began. If the mother started prenatal care later in the pregnancy, ask why it began at that time.

### Birth history

Ask about the labor and delivery to get a sense of whether there were any neonatal stressors that might have affected the infant's health. Was it an easy or difficult labor? Was the child delivered vaginally or by Caesarian section? Was the labor induced? Was the umbilical cord wrapped around the child's neck? Did the heart rate remain stable? Were there complications? Was a forceps used? Ask if the child was born full-term or whether the child was premature and by how much. Knowing about prematurity is essential for understanding the child's developmental status. Be sure to note this in the report and consider if any test scores need to be adjusted for prematurity (see chapter 2). Ask the parent about the child's birth weight, which hospital the child was born in, and how long the child remained in the hospital before discharge. If the child had an extended stay, why was this needed?

### Early developmental milestones

Early milestones are an important indicator of whether the child is developing appropriately. Often a parent will not remember exactly when these occurred. Ask the parent to give you her best estimate of the child's milestones. However, if the parent is quite unsure, then it is best simply to indicate this in your report rather than including information that is likely not accurate. Often children with delays in particular areas of development will also have been late in reaching their milestones. Key milestones that a parent is more likely to recall are when the child first walked and talked. Other key milestones include when the child first rolled over, crawled, sat up, and stood up.

### Medical history

Ask parents about the child's medical status. Find out if the child is healthy presently or has any medical conditions for which he is receiving any treatment, and for how long the condition has been present. Ask about both severe illnesses and any recurring mild conditions. Frequent ear infections, for example, may cause hearing loss and may indicate the need for a hearing test. When inquiring about previous conditions ask the parents if the child received medical care, or if they were taken to the emergency room. Does the child use the emergency room for routine care? Does the child require any special care at this time? Does the child require nursing care? If the child is medically fragile, document the child's medical needs, as this will be an important element of the IFSP plan when services are determined.

### Medication

Knowing if a child is taking medication will provide information about the child's health as well as about the child's performance during the evaluation. If a child is taking medication during the evaluation, it is important to indicate this in the report and to consider how this might impact on the child's performance. For example, we have had the experience of working with children who are taking asthma medication. Sometimes the parents tell us that their child is more active and irritable than usual. When this happens the evaluator should consider whether the evaluation is valid or whether it should be repeated at another time when the child is not taking medication. Certainly the evaluator should mention the issue of medication in the report and discuss how it affected the child's performance. Sometimes it may be necessary to contact the child's physician to get more information about the child's medical situation.

### Surgeries

Has the child had any surgeries and for what reasons? Did the surgery resolve the medical condition? Was hospitalization required? How old was the child when the surgery occurred?

### Hospitalizations

Did the child have any hospitalizations? If so, how old was the child, and how long was the hospitalization? What was the reason for the hospitalization? Was the condition resolved? Are there any current medical difficulties related to these hospitalizations?

### Allergies

Find out if there are any known allergies and, if so, how they affect the child.

### Vision

Be sure to ask about a child's vision. One of the authors learned from experience about the importance of asking this question early on in the evaluation process. After completing an evaluation of a 2-year-old girl, she was told by the mother that the little girl usually wore glasses, but they were being repaired. Because so many test items are visual, the evaluator had to return another day to redo the entire evaluation.

### Hearing

When evaluating young children who are learning to speak, there is often a question as to whether the child is having hearing difficulties. If there is any concern about hearing, the child should be immediately referred for an audiological examination. Sometimes, however, young children appear to have difficulty hearing but actually have difficulties in other areas, such as socialization and sensory processing. One common concern from parents of children with autism is "My child never responds when I call him." Evaluators need to determine whether behaviors such as this result from a hearing problem or from some other developmental difficulty.

### Additional Points

There are some additional points to consider regarding the developmental history. For example, it can be helpful to document the phone number of the pediatrician or other relevant health-care providers in case additional medical information is needed later on. Sometimes the parent has a copy of a physician's report that has not yet been shared with other EI staff, which can provide important information. Include any relevant details, such as the medical diagnosis and treatment recommendations. In addition, be aware that early developmental problems, such as complications at birth, can be followed by lawsuits. Report information accurately stating exactly who said what. For example, indicate as "parent report" what the parent told you. Additionally, if a parent does not recall something exactly, you can write that in your report. It's better to accept that the parent is unsure about a detail, such as a developmental milestone, than to push the parent to give you an exact date when she is not sure about it.

## DEVELOPMENTAL STATUS

In addition to looking at the child's family history and developmental history, the parent interview can yield a great deal of information about the child's developmental status. Although you may formally test the child, your findings need to be integrated with the parents report of the child's functioning, and your observations. Sometimes the child is not testable, and this is the only way to obtain information on the areas of functioning. Parents may also have concerns of their own that are not mentioned in the rating scales, which should be addressed. If you allow the interview to go beyond questions that are listed in a structured interview or a rating scale you will enhance your understanding of the child. Some of the most widely used structured parent interviews and rating scales are described in chapter 6.

We have divided the developmental status area of the interview into six sections referring to the five domains of development (cognitive, communication, daily living skills, socialization and motor), with the additional domain of sensory integration. Keep in mind that it is difficult to divide up a child's development into domains, as some skills belong to more than one domain. For example, the skill of "solving a puzzle" is both a cognitive skill and a fine motor skill. Thus, you may ask a question which we have listed under one domain, although it may really capture information relevant to several domains of functioning. Consider a question regarding how the child requests something. Is this a social or a communication skill? We feel it is both. You will have to use your professional experience and judgment to assess the responses of the parent and incorporate these in the appropriate part of your report.

When reviewing the following domains of functioning, keep in mind that not all questions are relevant for all children. We have listed key areas that you may wish to review with the parent. Choose the areas that you feel are most appropriate for the child with whom you are working. For example, you needn't ask about the child's ability to coo if the child is already speaking in sentences.

### Cognitive Functioning

Cognitive functioning refers to how the child thinks, solves problems, and understands concepts.

Cognitive functioning is one of the areas of early childhood development that is least well understood, as it encompasses many different types of skills and is quite complex. Most EI evaluators use a rating scale or test to assess this area. The test yields a score and a functional level for the child. However, at times parents will make statements about their child's cognitive skills. Be sure to listen to the parent and make sure you understand her perspective. If a parent says that her child is very smart, for example, ask her what the child does to show that he is smart. Some parents will describe behaviors that do indeed suggest that the child is demonstrating creativity or advanced thinking for his age. However, other parents will give examples that reveal that they may be overestimating their child's present abilities. Only by asking for the details can you make a more informed assessment of the child's development. Whether or not you agree with the parents' interpretation of their child's abilities, be open to hearing their observations. Give feedback that takes their observations into account and is sensitive to their concerns. In addition, be sure to include the parents' observations in your report.

The following are some areas of cognitive development that can be covered in a parent interview if insufficient information is obtained from formal testing or your observations.

Object permanence (e.g., looks for hidden object)

Using objects as tools (e.g., reaches for toy with a stick)

Number concepts (e.g., concept of one, rote counting, counting objects)

Matching (e.g., matches pictures, matches colors)

Problem solving (e.g., solves simple puzzles, puts objects in a form board)

Attention span (e.g., attends to a story, repeats number digits, pays attention when others talk to child)

Understands size concepts (e.g., big and little objects, big and little animals or people)

Understands concept of more and less (e.g., where there are more blocks or less blocks)

### Communication Skills

Communication skills refer to how the child expresses himself and his needs, and how he understands others.

A majority of young children are referred for evaluations because of concerns about their communication skills. Structured parent interviews used by special educators and psychologists usually have many questions about a child's language development. In addition, you may want to ask some of your own questions to be sure all the important areas are covered. If a language delay is suspected, then a speech evaluation should be conducted. The following are a list of some key areas to address regarding communication skills.

Vocalizing (cooing [vowel sounds like "oo"], babbling ["baba"], jargoning [similar to babbling, but sounding more like speech with adult-like inflection])

Expressive vocabulary (word approximations [e.g., "wa" for "water"], single words [e.g., "mama"], word combinations [e.g., "mama juice"], short phrases [several word combinations], sentences [longer combinations of words], size of vocabulary, how many words the child can say spontaneously)

Gestures (reaching up to be picked up, indicating yes or no by shaking head, pointing to what he wants)

Imitates sounds and words (e.g., says "how" or "wow" for dog, says "broom" for car)

Receptive vocabulary (knows some familiar objects, body parts, total number of words the child understands)

Follows simple 1-step directions (e.g., brings over toy when asked, without relying on parents' gestures)

Follows 2–3 step directions (e.g., "get your doll and give her some juice")

### Adaptive Skills

Adaptive skills refers to how the child performs self-care tasks, including eating, sleeping, toileting, dressing, and bathing.

This domain is also referred to as daily living skills or self-help skills. When assessing a child in this area, keep in mind that there are significant cultural differences in child rearing. For example, some cultures believe in toilet training early; others believe it is better to wait. In some cultures there is a high value placed on a young child developing self-care skills as early as possible. In other cultures a young child will be discouraged from eating by himself, and preference is given to adults showing their affection to the child by doing things for him, such as feeding him. Thus, a child's ability to perform a daily living skill may not only have to do with his abilities but also the parents' interest in teaching the skills. Sometimes, when asking about this, a parent will indicate that the child has unusual habits. For example, some children eat only certain foods and avoid others because of the texture of the food. Some children frequently smell their food. Whenever there is a report of something unusual, note it and ask relevant questions. This can help you determine whether there is a possibility of a developmental disorder such as autism or pervasive developmental disorder (see chapter 9). Some key areas of adaptive functioning include the following.

Sleeping (e.g., takes naps during the day, sleeps through the night, falls asleep on his own, any difficulties with sleep)

Feeding (e.g., sucks from breast or bottle, drinks from sippy cup, drinks from regular cup, eats strained foods, eats solid foods, eats a variety of solid foods, chews and swallows, uses spoon and fork, any feeding difficulties)

Toilet training (e.g., indicates by vocalizing when wet or soiled, uses potty or toilet)

Dressing (e.g., shows interest in changing wet or dirty clothes, removes a jacket or front-opening shirt by himself)

Washing (e.g., washes and dries hands, brushes teeth, helps with bathing self)

### Social-Emotional Functioning

Social-emotional functioning refers to how the child experiences and expresses emotions, and how he interacts with others and behaves.

This is a very challenging area to assess in very young children. Most young children have limited language skills, and even those who speak well do not describe their feelings directly. Thus, you must do your best to combine the parent report and your observations to create a cohesive picture of the child's social-emotional life. The best way to do this is to ask a variety of questions and to observe how the child behaves and interacts in a variety of contexts. Social-emotional functioning is likely the most difficult area to assess well with young children. The following are some important areas to address in your parent interview regarding this area of functioning.

Activity (e.g., high or low activity level)

Affect (e.g., laughing, smiling, frowning, appropriate response to a situation, serious expression, fearful expression)

Affection (e.g., gives hugs and kisses to family, gives hugs and kisses to strangers, accepts hugs and kisses from family, accepts hugs and kisses from strangers)

Aggressive behavior (e.g., hits, kicks, bites, pulls hair, chokes, pinches, head bangs, spits)

Attachment (e.g., clings to parent, separates from parent, shows fear of stranger appropriately or inappropriately, secure or insecure attachment to parent)

Attention span (e.g., focuses on activities, sits and listens to story, listens to a TV show, listens to directions)

Cooperation (e.g., engages willingly in activities, follows directions and requests)

Empathy (e.g., expresses concern when another person is hurt or unhappy)

Eye contact (e.g., looks at parents when they speak, looks at parent for approval, looks at others)

Fear (e.g., afraid of large animals, afraid of bugs, avoids dangerous situations, fearless)

Frustration tolerance (e.g., high or low frustration tolerance, persists when tasks are challenging, gets upset when asked to wait)

Helpfulness (e.g., offers assistance with chores, willing to help clean up toys)

Joint attention (this is when a child joins in looking at an object or activity with another person, e.g., looks at book with parent)

Mood (e.g., feeling sad, feeling happy, feeling angry, feeling afraid)

Sense of humor (e.g., laughs in response to seeing funny facial expression, laughs at peek-a-boo)

Social awareness (e.g., is aware of what others are doing around them)

Social interactions (e.g., shows interest in other children or adults, initiates interactions with others, responds to attempts at interactions from others, says hello to others)

Temperament (e.g., warms up easily to new people and situations, is even tempered, is quick to become irritated)

Transitioning ability (e.g., willingly follows daily routines, goes outside and comes back home without protest, turns off television without excessive protest, accepts parent request to change activity without much difficulty)

### *Motor Skills*

Motor skills refers to how the child is able to coordinate movements of his body and hands.

Structured parent interviews will have items concerning motor development. In addition, ask if the parent has any particular concerns regarding the child's motor skills. If the parent mentions any motor difficulties, or if you observe any motor difficulties, follow-up with questions regarding the frequency, duration, and intensity of these behaviors. The following are key areas to address.

#### Gross Motor Skills

Rolls (e.g., rolls from back to front, from front to back, rolls from right to left and vice versa)

Crawls (e.g., commando crawls [on stomach], crawls on all fours [without stomach touching the floor])

Sits (e.g., sits with support, sits without support)

Stands (e.g., stands holding on to furniture, stands independently)

Cruises (e.g., takes steps holding on to furniture)

Walks (e.g., takes one or two steps, walks sometimes, walks most of the time)

Climbs stairs (e.g., walks up stairs putting both feet on a step, walks up alternating feet, walks up and down stairs)

Runs (e.g., runs tentatively, runs without tripping or falling)

Climbs (e.g., climbs onto low furniture, climbs up high)

Jumps (e.g., jumps on two feet, hops on one foot while holding on)

## Fine Motor Skills

Reaching (e.g., reaches with one hand, reaches with two hands, reaches with coordination)

Grasping (e.g., holds object in hand, uses fist grip [grabs with whole hand], uses pincer grip [thumb and forefinger])

Release (e.g., voluntary, involuntary, accurate, using objects in desired target)

Transferring (e.g., transfers object from one hand to another)

Scribbling/copying (e.g., scribbles with crayon, draws a line or circle)

### Sensory Functions

Sensory functions have recently been given more attention as an important developmental area. Difficulties with sensory integration, one of the sensory functions, have been tied to pervasive developmental disorders. Key areas to address are indicated below and are based, in part, on the Infant/Toddler Sensory Profile (Psychological Corporation, 2002).

Sensory integration refers to how a child organizes and processes information through the environmental senses (vision, hearing, smell, taste) and the body senses (touch, proprioceptive, vestibular). Sensory modulation refers to how a child regulates and organizes sensations adaptively to a given situation. This can affect body awareness, movement levels, emotional responses, and attention. Sensory processing is the ability to register and interpret information via the senses. All of the sensory functions are assessed as they relate to the ability of a child to adapt to situations and daily life tasks.

Visual processing (e.g., makes appropriate eye contact, looks at reflection in the mirror)

Auditory processing (e.g., responds when name is called, responds appropriately to sounds, attends to voices)

Vestibular processing (e.g., does not mind being moved, engages in an appropriate amount of physical activity, does not engage in excessive spinning or rocking)

Tactile processing (e.g., notices wet or dirty diapers; likes being cuddled; willing to crawl and walk on different surfaces; willing to touch objects of various textures; does not mind tags in clothing; reacts appropriately to pressure, pain, changes in temperature; does not mind creams and oils)

Oral-sensory processing (e.g., tries new foods, does not chew or lick non-food items)

Olfactory issues (e.g., smells food appropriately, does not engage in excessive smelling of food or objects, especially objects that do not have an odor, such as plastic toys)

Proprioception/Kinesthesia (e.g., being able to move through space, appropriate equilibrium responses, providing postural security and stability)

# VI

# Formal Testing, Tests, and Measures

## Overview

The formal evaluation assesses the child's development by engaging him in a variety of age-specific tasks. We have worked with many different children from a variety of different backgrounds. All children are unique and require an individualized approach. However, we have found that some ways of working are generally more effective than others. The following are our suggestions for how to conduct the formal evaluation.

## Working with the Child on the Floor

In working with very young children we have found it easiest for the child, and most productive for the evaluator, to sit on the floor. The young child usually feels most comfortable on the floor, where he can move around easily and where the evaluator is down at his level (Greenspan & Wieder, 1998). To help the child focus on tasks and to define your work area, you may want to bring a small rug to place on the floor. If you sit with your back to the wall, you will have a complete view of the child and it will prevent the child from running around behind you. Sometimes it can also work well to sit with a young child at a child-sized table if the child is approaching age three.

## Presenting Testing Materials

It is best to present one item or toy at a time to the child. Keeping the other items concealed will prevent the child from getting distracted. Some children get attached to a particular item and are unwilling to proceed unless that item remains in their possession. Use your judgment as to how best to handle this situation. You might allow the child to continue playing with this toy but also add a new toy. If the child plays for a long time with the same toy and does not show interest in other toys, you may need to take that toy away. We have found that with experience we are usually able to help the child make the transition from one activity to another. If a child has difficulty transitioning between tasks, make sure to note it. Also check with the parents to see if this is typical of his behavior.

## Involving Parents in the Formal Evaluation

Parents are an essential part of the Early Intervention evaluation and should be included in each step of the process. Involving the parents in the evaluation is helpful for both the child and the parents. Children will tend to give a more optimal performance when they feel supported by their parents. Parents will also be more accepting of the evaluator's results and recommendations if they have witnessed their child's performance directly. For these reasons, we feel parents need to be present during the evaluation. The parents can be involved in the evaluation in a few important ways:

1)  If the child does not appear to be responding freely to you the evaluator, a parent may administer some evaluation items to the child. Parent involvement is particularly helpful with verbal items, such as when you ask the child to label pictures of familiar objects. You may need to help direct the parents and give them specific instructions about what you want them to do—or not to do. For example, you may want them to ask a question exactly, but not give hints to the child or help them perform a task.

2)  The parents may provide emotional support for the child during the testing situation. Depending on the needs of the child, this may involve holding him on their lap, sitting close to the child, or giving verbal encouragement. Having parents say "good job," or clapping can easily turn a frown into a smile.

3)  At times the parents may be needed as interpreters of the child's language and behavior. Children with language delays may be difficult to understand, and the parents may be called on to translate. Children may also display behaviors that are

confusing to you, and you may need to ask the parents to explain. For example, a child may suddenly begin to suck his thumb in the middle of the evaluation. In order to understand this behavior, the evaluator might ask the parents if the child does this at other times, or if this means the child is perhaps feeling tired or anxious.

Parent involvement is crucial to a successful evaluation. However, it is also important that the child complete as many of the evaluation items as possible on his own. Out of anxiety, parents sometimes try to help with evaluation items or try to direct their child so that he will complete items successfully. In a gentle, empathic way, encourage the parents to allow the child to work on his own. Only ask the parents to administer a test item if it is necessary as a way to engage the child. You can remind the parents that in order to understand the child's development, you need to see what the child can do.

## *Eliciting Optimal Performance from the Child*

When evaluating older children and adults, the reliability of the testing is usually considered crucial. This means that the testing experience is designed so that the individual will perform similarly if tested repeatedly with the same measure (test-retest reliability). To ensure test-retest reliability, the evaluation should be given in the exact same manner each time to each individual. With young children, this is not considered as important as it is with older children or adults. Rather, obtaining the child's optimal performance is the goal. This may involve giving a test item in a nonstandard way (e.g., the parent may give the item). Since infants and young children tend to be unpredictable and impulsive, the testing procedure may have to be altered in order to gain their cooperation. Some professionals believe that formal testing has only a very limited role in early childhood assessment process. They believe that formal testing should only be done after a developmental history is taken and a series of observations of the child with the caregiver and with the evaluator are done (Greenspan & Weider, 1998). A series of sessions certainly can give more information about the child and can aid your work. However, we believe that a single evaluation session, conducted effectively, can yield adequate information with which to assess the child thoroughly and provide good information about a child's functioning. When the results of the evaluation are not optimal, the evaluator always has the option of scheduling an additional evaluation session.

***Establish Rapport with the Parents***. In order to elicit optimal performance from the child, it is helpful to establish rapport with both the parents and the child. It is usually helpful to establish rapport with the parents first. This is why we recommend that you complete the parent interview prior to evaluating the child. After the child sees that his parents are comfortable with you, he will usually find it easier to begin to trust you.

***Engaging the Child***. Often a child will approach you on his own once he sees that his parents are comfortable. If the child does not approach you after a while, you may need to make overtures toward him. It is best to talk to the child in a cheerful but quiet manner, so that the child is interested but not intimidated. You may need to take out a toy to entice the child. You may also need to ask the parent to become involved in encouraging the child to participate in the evaluation. It usually helps if the parent sits with you on the floor with the child.

***Ways to Elicit Cooperation***. Sometimes the child may not want to participate in the evaluation, and it may take an extra effort to gain his cooperation. There are many ways to elicit cooperation. Some of these include asking about one of his toys; playing peek-a-boo; joining in an activity he is doing; asking him to show you his toys; taking out blocks, dolls, or other toys; asking him to label body parts; and exploring his toys with him. Keep in mind that it is best to try to select toys that are developmentally appropriate to the age of the child you are evaluating.

***Do Less Challenging Tasks First***. To ensure an optimal performance from the child, you should start the formal evaluation with the less challenging, more appealing items. For children with language delays, this typically means beginning with non-verbal tasks, (i.e., those relying more on motor skills, such as blocks and puzzles.) For children with motor delays, it may mean beginning with an item involving pictures or words, as they may not be able to reach, grasp, or move easily. Some children will become engaged more easily by toys that move or make noise. Once the child is comfortable and fully engaged in the evaluation process, it will be easier for him to attempt more challenging tasks.

***Repeating Items***. With young children it may also be necessary at times to repeat items. This is usually permissible on formal measures designed for testing young children. Items may be repeated if, for example, a child is temporarily distracted or if he seems to have difficulty understanding the evaluation directions. Check with the test manual of the test you are giving to learn if that particular test allows for items to be repeated.

***Pacing***. The evaluator will need to adjust the pace of the evaluation to the particular needs of each child. Some children perform best when items are presented slowly. More typically, young children perform best when items are presented at a steady pace with little delay between items. If a child is somewhat overactive, then items may need to be presented more quickly. Young children often need to move around during the testing situation. This may mean crawling away from the examiner or walking into the kitchen to get a drink. The key to testing very young children is to be flexible and to go with the flow as much as you reasonably can. Keep in mind that most young children have a much shorter attention span than older children or adults. So, work quickly!

***Encouragement and Praise***. In order to ensure an optimal performance from each child, give the child frequent encouragement and praise. This is important even if the child is unable to complete many items successfully. Children may be given praise purely for attempting an item. If a child misses many items at age level, the evaluator may want to administer some easier items, so that the child can experience some success during the testing session. By encouraging and praising the child, the evaluator may also serve as a positive role model for parents. Don't hesitate to clap for the child or give an enthusiastic "yeah" or "good job." Experienced evaluators testing older children may have been told not to give praise only for correct responses so as not to bias the children or make them feel badly when they do not perform an item correctly (Sattler, 2001). This generally does not apply to very young children. Infants and toddlers need a lot of encouragement and praise for their effort, in order to sustain their interest in the evaluation.

***Involving Interested Siblings***. Although working with the child alone is often ideal, in practice this is often not possible or practical. It is very common for siblings to be present during the evaluation of a young child. Rather than ignoring the siblings or asking the parents to keep them in another room, the authors have found it helpful to involve them in the evaluation process. When parents send the siblings out of the room, you will inevitably hear crying and whining before long. Involving siblings not only avoids these conflicts, it can help a withdrawn child to be more comfortable with the evaluator. It is a challenging task for an evaluator to involve interested siblings without distracting the child being evaluated, however. Siblings might try to take over the testing, or they might try to show their brother or sister how to complete tasks. It is usually best if the evaluator tells the siblings that they can play with the evaluation materials after the child being evaluated is done. Sometimes a sibling can be given a different toy to play with on the side. You may be able to get the children to take turns with a toy, giving it first to the child who is being evaluated—ideally. At other times, you may want to say, "let's watch Ashley try this one."

# Tests and Measures

The Early Intervention evaluation includes a variety of formal assessment measures. Some are standardized and normed, others are criterion-referenced. Normed tests are those in which a child's performance can be compared with a normed group, usually a representative national sample of children. The normed measures are useful for comparing children of the same age, and for determining the extent to which a child may deviate from normal development. However, when working with very young children it is important to take into account the difficulties involved in trying to have them follow standardized procedures. You can obtain a more accurate picture of the child when you fully take into account the child's particular needs and style of functioning. You need to integrate the formal test findings with information obtained from the parent interview and informal assessment.

## Recommended Early Childhood Tests, Structured Interviews, and Measures

The assessment measures most commonly used by special educators and psychologists in the Early Intervention Program are listed below.

**Test Name:**
**Bayley Scales of Infant Development—Second Edition** (BSID-II)

Author: Nancy Bayley (1993)

Publisher: The Psychological Corporation, San Antonio, Texas; (800) 872-1726, www.psychcorp.com

Age Range: birth to 3.6 years

Administration Time: 25-60 minutes

**Description**: The BSID II is a standardized assessment measure for evaluating young children. It includes items covering the areas of cognition, language, motor and personal-social development. It contains three scales: the mental scale, the motor scale, and the behavior rating scale. The mental scale is often used for developmental or psychological assessments. It contains 22 item sets designated by age, with an average of 27 items per set. Items are organized by chronological age and increase in difficulty. The scale produces a standardized score for overall cognitive development. As of this writing, the BSID III is in development.

**Administration**: Administration of the BSID II requires training and experience evaluating infants and toddlers. The administration of items is complex, because the test involves many tasks with multiple trials. The sequence of item administration can be varied, depending on the needs of the individual child. Examiners typically have master's or doctoral-level training, in accordance with the guidelines of the American Psychological Association.

**Scoring**: Evaluators need to have experience with many children before being able to reliably score the BSID II. Once a score (of either 0 or 1) for each item has been determined, the raw score, index score, and developmental age can be easily calculated. There is also space to note the quality of the child's performance and whether they cooperated with or refused each task.

## Test Name:
## Hawaii Early Learning Profile 0-3 (HELP)

Publisher: VORT Publishing, Palo Alto, CA. (1995); (650) 322-8282, www.vort.com

Age Range: Birth to 3 years

Administration Time: approximately 30 minutes

**Test Description**: The HELP was developed at the University of Hawaii. It is a curriculum-based assessment for evaluating children and covers 685 skills in the six domains: cognitive, language, gross motor, fine motor, social, and self-help. It is not standardized but is used to identify needs and track development. It engages the child in a series of play-based activities appropriate to each stage of development. It involves a combination of child observations and parent interview. The HELP is frequently used by special educators, but can also be used by professionals from different disciplines. It is easy to use and easy to understand by parents.

**Administration**: The Hawaii Early Learning Profile can initially present a challenge to evaluators because it contains many items for each age level and domain. It does not involve specific test materials; evaluators use their own materials to assess the child's functioning on a variety of tasks.

**Scoring**: The clinician identifies which items a child is able to perform or not yet able to perform.

**Test Name:**
**The Vineland Adaptive Behavior Scales**

Authors: Sparrow, Balla & Cicchetti (1984)

Publisher: American Guidance Service; (800) 328-2560, www.agsnet.com

Age Range: Birth through adulthood

Administration Time: 20 to 60 minutes

**Test Description**: The Vineland Adaptive Behavior Scales is a structured interview measure designed to assess personal and social functioning. It asks about the individual's functioning in the four domains of communication, daily living skills, socialization, and motor skills. It provides standard scores, percentile ranks, and age equivalents for each domain of functioning.

**Administration**: The Vineland Adaptive Behavior Scales involve a limited number of questions regarding each domain of development. Evaluators must be trained in how to interview the parent in a way that reveals accurate information about the child.

**Scoring**: Children are rated from 0-3 on whether they can perform each skill "always, sometimes or never."

**Note**: The Vineland Adaptive Behavior Scales were used in the design of a newer version focusing on early childhood, from birth to 5 years, 11 months (Vineland Social-Emotional Early Childhood Scales).

*Test Name:*
*The Childhood Autism Rating Scales* (CARS)

Authors: Schopler, Reichler & Renner (1986)

Publisher: Western Psychological Corporation, Los Angeles, CA; (800) 648-8857, www.wpspublish.com

Age Range: all ages

Administration Time: approximately 20 minutes

*Description*: The CARS is a behavioral rating scale for children ages 2 years and older. The child is rated on 15 items based on an interview with the parents and clinical observations. The items cover the following areas: relating to people, imitation, emotional response, body use, object use, adaptation to change, visual response, listening response, taste, smell and touch response, fear or nervousness, verbal communication, nonverbal communication, activity level, and level and consistency of intellectual response.

*Administration*: The CARS can be administered by a psychologist, or trained teacher.

*Scoring*: The child receives a score of 1-4 on each item, and their total score is the sum of scores on all items. A score of 15-29.5 is considered to be in the Non-Autistic range, 30-36.5 is the Mild to Moderately Autistic range, and 37-60 is the Severely Autistic range.

## Additional Tests and Measures

The following is a list of additional commonly used early childhood evaluation measures. Each one has a manual or article that explains how to administer the measure and interpret the results. Additional classes, workshops or consultations with experienced professionals can provide more detailed information about how best to use and interpret these measures. For a more extensive review of early childhood tests see Grant & Nozyce (2001).

***Batelle Developmental Inventory*** (Newborg, Stock, & Wnek, 1984) is a comprehensive instrument that can be used for screening, diagnosis, evaluation, and program development of children from birth to age 3. The complete BDI contains 341 items; it also has a screening test, which contains 96 items.

***Child Behavior Checklist*** (Achenbach & Edelbrook, 1986) is a rating scale filled out by parents, teachers, and other caregivers to describe the behavior of children ages 2 and older. The measure covers seven domains of behavior.

***Cognitive Abilities Scale 2*** (Bradley-Johnson & Johnson, 2001) is designed to measure current intellectual level in children ages 3 months to 3 years and 11 months. The test yields a General Cognitive Quotient and a Nonvocal Cognitive Quotient.

***Denver Developmental Screening Test II*** (Frankenburg, Dodd, Archer, Bresnick, Maschaka, Edeman, & Shapiro, 1990) is a popular screening instrument used to detect problems or delays which should be more fully evaluated later. It measures four areas: personal/social, fine-motor/adaptive, language, and gross motor and is often used by pediatrician to screen infants and toddlers.

***Gesell Developmental Scales*** were designed to assess the development of infants and preschoolers (ages 4 weeks to 6 years) and to diagnose developmental delays and problems.

**Griffiths Developmental Scale** (Bailey, & Bricker, 1986) was first published in 1954 for the purpose of assessing cognitive development in infants ages 0 to 2. In 1967 it was expanded to include children from 2 to 8 years of age, and revised and renormed in 1980.

**Infant-Toddler Developmental Assessment** (IDA) (Provence, Erikson, Vater, & Palermi, 1995) is designed to identify children from birth to age three who are developmentally at risk. It takes into account health, family, and social-emotional factors and collects data from multiple sources, including parents and previous evaluations.

**Kaufman Assessment Battery for Children** (Kaufman & Kaufman, 1983) measures both intelligence and achievement in children from age 2 years 6 months to 12 years 6 months. It allows the evaluator flexibility in administration and attempts to minimize the effects of cultural differences.

**Mullen Scales of Early Learning** (Mullen, 1995) assesses cognitive abilities in the areas of visual, linguistic, and motor functioning in children ages 0 to 68 months.

*VII.*

# Informal Assessment of Behavior, Social-Emotional Functioning, and Play Skills

## Overview

In addition to interviewing the parent and using formal measures of assessment, you need to rely on your observations of the child. Your observations are informed by your experience with young children and your knowledge of child development. The informal evaluation looks at the child's behavior, social-emotional functioning, interactions with others, spontaneous play, and covers some of the areas that may not be adequately assessed through the parent interview or formal testing. The informal evaluation is particularly important to include, because young children may not perform at their best on formal measures. Young children may be unaccustomed to a structured testing situation— they may be timid or fearful, and they may only show their true colors during free play or interactions with their caregiver. Some children, because of social or behavioral issues, may be unable to engage in structured tasks and may only show their skills when left on their own.

## Behavior and Social Skills

When conducting developmental and psychological evaluations it is particularly important to give a complete assessment of the child's behavior and social skills. The following are some of the key areas to observe throughout the evaluation session.

*Activity*. When observing a child's activity level, it is necessary to think of how the child compares to his peers. A child can only be active, overactive, or slow to respond when compared with other children his own age. If you write in your evaluation report that the child is "very active," a reader may respond, "Of course he is very active. He's two years old—what do you expect?" You need to develop experience so you can say with confidence not just that a child is very active, but that he is "very active, even when compared to the typically developing child of his age."

**Affect and mood**. Affect refers to the extent to which a child is emotionally expressive. For example, a child may smile frequently or laugh. A child may frown, cry, or have a tantrum. Affect is the child's outward expression of emotion (e.g., smiling, frowning). Mood refers to the inner emotional experience of the child. The easiest way to assess the child's mood is by observing the child's outward expression. However, it is important to check in with the parents in order to get a more complete sense of the child's emotional experience. Some children, for example, may smile only slightly during the evaluation because of shyness around the evaluator. When the parents are asked, however, they may say that the child is usually cheerful and expressive. Some children will display affect that does not seem appropriate to the situation. For example, they will scream repeatedly or laugh for no apparent reason. Note and consider this when making a diagnosis of a developmental disorder.

**Affection**. Notice if the child accepts affection from caregivers, or if he prefers to seek attention or affection from you. Some children will give affection when they feel like it, but be resistant to accepting affection or physical contact from others. It is natural for young children not to be affectionate with evaluators, as they are unfamiliar people. If the child is very affectionate without discretion, this is worth noting.

**Aggressive behavior**. Sometimes you will observe aggressive behavior during the evaluation, such as hitting, kicking or biting. Ask the parent whether this behavior is typical. Often, when you see aggressive behavior, the parent will also report that the child is aggressive. If the parent says that the child is not usually aggressive, you need to consider why the child was acting this way on the day of testing. Compare the child's behavior during the session to that reported by the parent and try to understand why there may be differences between those situations.

***Attachment***. Attachment is the need young children have for a close relationship with a primary caregiver (Lieberman, 1993). Attachment behavior can be observed in many ways. It can be observed in the interactions the child has with his parents, such as the way the child reaches for his parents, hugs, kisses, or holds them. A child can also demonstrate attachment behavior in the way he responds to unfamiliar people. For example, does he cry or cling to his parents when he sees the evaluator? Does he periodically check in with his parents as he is performing activities, or does he ignore his parents altogether? When the child needs comfort during the evaluation, does he seek out his parents, look to the evaluator, or try to soothe himself? The development of secure attachment behavior is considered one of the most important accomplishments of early childhood. Insecure attachment is also notable and should be included in your findings.

***Attention span.*** Evaluating a child's attention span can be difficult. The only way to know if a child has a short, average, or long attention span is to compare the child with other children of the same age. The ability to make this comparison comes from experience with young children. The more infants and toddlers that you observe and assess, the easier it will be to say with confidence that a particular child has a very short attention span "compared with the typically developing child his age." Note that a child's attention may be situation specific, or specific to certain kinds of activities. For example, the child may be very active and unfocused during the parent interview, but then calm down and pay attention quite well during the formal assessment, which is a much more structured situation. The child may focus well when working with toys and playing with manipulatives. However, he might not pay attention and "turn off" when given verbal tasks or shown pictures.

***Cooperation***. Was the child cooperative during the evaluation? Did he participate willingly in activities? Did he engage more easily in manipulative tasks or verbal tasks? Did he purposely not complete a task, or could it be that he did not understand the directions? Did he cooperate with his parents and follow their directions?

115

**Empathy**. Even at a young age, some children show concern when another person is hurt or unhappy. This involves being able to take the perspective of another person. During the evaluation, you may see this in terms of the child's reaction to the parents' or siblings' emotional states. For example, a child may approach his mother or watch her intently if she is crying. Another child may try to help a younger sibling who falls down.

**Eye contact**. The extent to which a child displays eye contact is very important in assessing his ability to interact with others. It is also helpful in making a diagnosis of autism or pervasive developmental disorder. Check to see if the child's eye contact is consistent or inconsistent, or whether the child avoids making eye contact altogether. Does the child look at one person but not others? Some children will make eye contact with their parents but not with an unfamiliar adult. Try to develop hypotheses about whether limited eye contact may be due to shyness, or possibly due to interpersonal difficulties that should be assessed further.

**Fear**. This may be hard to assess during the evaluation if the child is in a familiar setting with a sympathetic caregiver. However, you may be able to assess whether the child is afraid of you, of the caregiver, or of any particular sensory experience, such as a loud noise. Sometimes a child may be excessively fearful of the evaluator and cling to his caregiver or hide when you arrive.

**Frustration tolerance**. The testing situation will usually give you the opportunity to witness how the child deals with frustration. When the child is given challenging tasks, he will either persist at trying to complete them, try them and give up, or reject them altogether. Some children will become angry when a task is challenging; other children will calmly proceed.

**Helpfulness**. During the evaluation, some children will make a concerted effort to be helpful. They will put evaluation materials back in their bags and hand you toys when they are finished. They may also be observed helping their parents clean up. Other children will not show interest in being helpful.

*Joint attention*. This refers to the child's ability to focus on the same object or activity with another person. Examples of engaging in joint attention would be the child looking at a book when you are reading to him, having the child engage in an activity with you, and playing a game together such as rolling a ball back and forth (Wetherby & Prizant, 2000).

*Sense of humor*. Very young children often display a delightful sense of humor. For example, they will initiate peek-a-boo with you, or they may do something such as knocking down a tower of blocks and then laugh about it. This is usually a positive sign of their cognitive and social development.

*Social awareness*. When you open your toy bag, does the child dive into it, trying to grab as many toys as possible? Does the child wait to be given a toy? Does the child say "please" or "thank you"? Does the child wave good-bye? Does the child spend most of the session involved with objects, or is he also interested in watching what other people are doing? These observations give important clues as to the child's awareness of social customs.

*Social interactions*. The testing situation will give you the opportunity to observe the child interacting with his caregivers, possibly his siblings, and with you (an unfamiliar adult). It will give you a sense of how the child separates from his caregivers and how he responds to strangers. There are many types of social interactions, such as interactions with peers, which you will probably not observe in a testing situation, and therefore you must rely on the parent interview to enhance your understanding of the child's functioning in this area. Occasionally, you may need to do a classroom observation in order to get a more complete assessment of the child's social interactions.

*Temperament*. This refers to the child's innate tendency to react in certain ways. These tendencies are thought to be fairly stable over the course of development. Some important temperamental types are described as "easy," "slow to warm up," "difficult," and "active"

(Lieberman, 1993). During the evaluation, you may see "easy" children who adapt quickly to the testing situation and happily engage in any type of activity. Other, "difficult" children may be irritable and may be easily upset or frustrated. Children who are "slow to warm up" may initially withdraw or stay close to their parents, until they have had time to get used to you. Then, after observing you for a while they may engage willingly in activities. Active children may warm up quickly, but race through activities to get to the next novel item.

*Transitioning ability*. The child's ability to transition from one activity to another is one indication of his flexibility and adaptability. This becomes particularly important when the child is involved in a group activity or a classroom setting. You can observe transitioning ability by watching to see if the child easily goes from one activity to the next during the evaluation. Does the child easily accept a new toy or does he refuse to give up a favorite toy?

## Assessment of Play

An assessment of play skills is another important component of the informal evaluation. A review of the research on play has shown that a child's level of play is a good indicator of his cognitive and representational abilities (Vig, 1997-1998). Play assessments are a particularly useful way of assessing representational skills in preverbal children. In addition, children who are resistant to formal testing may be more likely to engage in a free play session. A number of authors have described the development of play in early childhood as proceeding in a predictable sequence. The following is an outline of some of the important stages of play development, as described by Belsky and Most (1981):

1.  *mouthing of toys* (indiscriminate mouthing of materials)

2.  *simple manipulation* (turning over an object; looking at and touching an object)

3.  *functional* (manipulation that is particularly appropriate for a certain object, e.g., pushing buttons on a toy phone, pushing a car along the floor)

4.  ***relational functional*** (bringing together two toys in an appropriate manner, e.g., setting a cup on a saucer, placing a peg into a pegboard)

5.  ***pretend self*** (pretend behavior directed toward the self, e.g., pretending to drink from a cup, pretending to talk on phone)

6.  ***pretend other*** (pretend behavior directed toward another, e.g., feeding a doll with a spoon, brushing a doll's hair)

7.  ***sequence pretend*** (repetition of a pretend act with minor variation or a link to a different pretend scheme, e.g., drinking from a bottle and then giving a doll a drink, putting a doll in a cradle and then kissing it goodnight)

## Popular Play Scales

Researchers going back to Jean Piaget (1936) have been interested in observing children and their play skills to assess their development. Here are a few of the more commonly used play scales that can be used to assess a child's development as reflected in his play.

***Westby Play Scale*** (Westby, 1980). One of the older and more popular play scales was developed by Westby. This scale presents ten stages of play development that a child should achieve between the ages of 9 months and 5 years. Evaluators use their own toys and present their own sequence of activities to determine the child's level of play. This is based on Westby's clinical work and observations and is not normed. It is used extensively, as it is relatively easy to use and score.

***Transdisciplinary Play-Based Assessment*** (Linder, 1993). This approach, for children from infancy to age 6, uses specific observational guidelines to assess cognitive, social-emotional, communication, language, and sensorimotor development during a play session.

***Symbolic Play Test*** (Lowe & Costello, 1988). This measure presents the child with four different sets of toys and allows the child to play freely with the toys. The child is then given a raw score based on the types of activities he exhibits with the toys during a 10-15 minute session. This measure, which is not normed, is appropriate for children ages 12 to 36 months.

*VIII.*

# Closing Discussion with Parents

## Last Questions to Parents

Information from the parent is obtained during the parent interview and during the entire evaluation session. Since you are usually only seeing the child for one testing session, it is important to get as much information as possible from the parent about how the child functions in general, not just on the day of the evaluation. Then, before leaving the home, be sure to ask the parents three important questions:

> Did your child behave typically today?
> Is there anything else you want to share about your child?
> Do you have any questions for me?

## Validity of Evaluation

If the parent responds that the child behaved in a typical manner, then this supports the validity of the evaluation findings. If the parent says the child was not behaving in a typical manner, you need to find out what it was about the child's functioning that was different, and whether it was different enough to change the results of the evaluation. Often it turns out that the child's performance on a few items was not typical, but the parent believes that the rest of the evaluation results are valid. If the parent feels that overall the child's performance was not typical, then you must find out why she thought this was the case. You may need to plan for another test session to redo the evaluation if the parent feels the session definitely did not reflect the child's typical functioning. Ideally, the parents will finish the session feeling that the child behaved typically, if not optimally. In many cases, we find the parent says she felt the child performed better than she had expected.

## Situational Factors

Even if the evaluator attempts to make the evaluation situation as comfortable as possible for the child, it is nevertheless an unfamiliar situation with a new adult. Some children have never been exposed to the types of materials and toys that the evaluator presents. Some have rarely been in a situation where an adult sat down with them on the floor to play. Because of these factors, young children may be more anxious, fearful, quiet, or hesitant than they are during their usual daily activities. Alternatively, they may be excited, happy, and eager to participate in new activities. While some children will cry when you enter the home, others will cry when you leave. When you assess the child's functioning, you must take these factors into account and consider the impact of the testing situation on the child's behavior. This is often an important part of the closing discussion with the parents, who may wonder if the results reflect the child's typical or optimal functioning.

## Answering the Parents' Questions

Here are some typical questions asked by parents, and suggestions for how to respond to them.

### Is my child delayed?

Parents want to know if their child is delayed. If you feel confident that the child is or is not delayed, you will want to share this information with the parent. You want to be careful, however, not to commit to any specific information about the extent of the delay before you have scored and reviewed all your measures. It is very awkward and unsettling if the parent is given information verbally at the end of the evaluation which is then contradicted in your report.

### Why does my child have this problem?

We usually do not know the answer to this question. There are some developmental disorders associated with medical conditions, and some with a genetic cause (e.g., Down's syndrome). However, there are many cases in which a child has a developmental delay and the cause is simply not known.

### Will my child receive Early Intervention services?

You cannot answer this question with a simple yes or no, since the evaluator does not directly approve services. That is the role of the EIOD, the representative of the Early Intervention program. It is best to tell the parent that this will be decided when all of the evaluation results are completed and reviewed at the IFSP meeting.

### Will my child always be delayed?

The truth is that nobody can predict the future, and nobody can tell with certainty how a child will develop in the future. However, we know that intervention helps. Thus, we recommend that you emphasize the benefits of early intervention services (if offered) and that this is a good way to stimulate the child's development. In addition, you can explain to the parents that the child's development will be monitored throughout the early intervention program and can be formally evaluated again before age 3 to determine his progress and needs.

### Will my child need Special Education?

Certainly, we cannot determine if a child will need special education in the future. However, the best way to help the child and perhaps to avoid future special education needs is to provide the appropriate level of care as early as possible.

### Is it my fault that my child is delayed?

In the vast majority of cases, a child's delay is not related to anything that the parent did or did not do. However, it is common for many parents to wonder if they contributed in some way to their child's developmental disability. At other times, other family members or other people may suggest to the parents that it is their fault. This is rarely true, however. Usually only in rare instances, such as in severe cases of child abuse or neglect, can parents' behavior be tied to a child's developmental delays.

### If I played with him more, would he be alright now?

This is another question that suggests that parents may feel guilty about their child's problems. Yes, it helps to work with, play with, and to teach a child. However, children are like sponges, and even without teaching them, they learn a great deal on their own, absorbing all kinds of information from the world around them. The parents behavior is rarely to blame for a child's significant developmental delays.

### What can I do for my child?
The best thing a parent can do is to complete the evaluation process rapidly and to obtain the appropriate services. The role of the services is not only to provide direct assistance to the child, but to work with the parents to give them information on how best to help their child.

### What can I do now before the services begin?
Parents can research the condition or diagnosis provided for the child and can stay in touch with the service coordinator, so that they can make any arrangements needed for services to begin. When the child begins services, professionals will provide the parents with activities and ways to work with the child at home.

### Are there any books I can read or products to purchase to help me with my child?
There are many books and materials that can assist parents in learning about child development. There are also many products specifically designed to be both fun and educational for young children. Most important, however, is that the parent or caregivers interact with the child and provide a caring as well as a stimulating environment. This kind of environment can be created using a variety of materials, toys, and activities. Materials need not be expensive or specifically packaged as "educational." See our website for links to other sites offering books or materials.

## Informing Parents of Your Impressions and Recommendations

At the end of the evaluation, it is important to check in with the parents one last time. This is when you will get some final input about the child and then be able to briefly discuss your impressions. It is important to provide feedback at this time, to ease the parents' anxieties and to give them an idea of what will be presented in your report. If feedback is given in a clear and sensitive manner, it can help make it easier for the parents to understand and accept the evaluation when it is presented at the IFSP meeting. Informing parents briefly about their child at the end of the evaluation also gives them additional time to think about the types of interventions they would like for their child.

By the end of the evaluation session, you and the parents will ideally have reached a common understanding about how the child is functioning. If you have communicated with the parents throughout the evaluation session, and if you have pointed out important aspects of the child's performance to the parents during the evaluation, it is more likely that they will be in agreement with you by the end of the evaluation. The parents will then be in a better position to understand the evaluator's impressions and recommendations in the report. This is also an opportunity to check in with the parents regarding whether they agree with your impressions. If they do not agree, then this is an important time to discuss any of their concerns or questions.

Here are some recommendations for giving feedback to parents:

**Be Brief**. Feedback to parents should only involve a brief description of your impressions. You do not want to give too much information to the parents before reviewing the test results carefully and before consulting with other team members. We recommend that you present general impressions rather than specific test findings to the parents at this time. It usually takes some time to calculate the scores, and it could be very disturbing to parents to be told something during the evaluation and then to read something different in the report. In addition, you can expect parents to be quite anxious before, during and after the evaluation. Sometimes, in an effort to calm their anxieties with explanations, you can have the opposite effect and actually leave them feeling more anxious. Ask the parents if they agree with your impressions so you may address any differerences at that point.

**Mention Strengths First**. When giving feedback, begin by describing the child's areas of strength. This can alleviate some of the parents' initial anxiety. It tells parents that you see positive aspects of their child and his development, and it can make it easier for them to accept your evaluation of the child's delays or difficulties.

***Don't Avoid Telling Parents About a Developmental Delay***. Parents should be informed at this time if their child performed significantly below age level in some areas. This should be done with sensitivity to the parents' reactions. Sometimes parents are aware of the difficulties and sometimes they are not. In either case, it is helpful for them to hear from your general impressions, so they will not be surprised when the results of the evaluation are presented in more detail in the report and during the IFSP meeting. When discussing the child's areas of delay, you should be sure that the parents understand your impressions. In addition, you should have some certainty about your results. If you do not feel confident about your impressions, then do not give feedback until you have thoroughly analyzed your findings and written your report.

***Carefully Address Parents' Questions About Their Child's Need for Developmental Services***. Usually, one of the parents' main concerns is whether their child is delayed and needs services. You can answer this question clinically. You can inform the parents if you feel the child has any developmental delays. However, even if you believe the child has some delays, he may or may not qualify for services under the Early Intervention Program. This is an important distinction. Give the parents your impressions about the child's needs, but make sure they understand that only the Early Intervention official will approve early intervention services.

***Inform Parents About the Next Steps***. The end of the evaluation is the appropriate time to set the stage for the next steps in the process. You can explain to the parents that they will receive a copy of all the evaluation reports (usually by mail) prior to the IFSP meeting. Sometimes, informing meetings are also held at the evaluation agency prior to the IFSP meeting to review the evaluations with the parents. If not, the reports are presented at the IFSP meeting, either by the evaluators themselves or by representatives of the evaluation agency. Before leaving the home, the evaluator should also remind parents that they can contact the evaluation agency if they have further questions. It is a good idea to leave your business card, so the parents can follow-up with you or your agency.

*IX.*

# How to Identify Autism and Pervasive Developmental Disorders in Early Childhood

## Challenges of Assessing Autism and Pervasive Developmental Disorders

One of the most important tasks of early childhood assessment is to identify autism and pervasive developmental disorder (PDD) at an early age. The earlier the child's difficulties are identified, the earlier services can begin, usually with better outcomes. This is a difficult challenge for several reasons. First, the younger children are, the more they are changing, developing, and the bigger the range of what is normal. Second, without a high level of experience evaluating young children it is difficult to know when to make a definitive diagnosis. Third, it is a very difficult task to inform parents that their child may have a developmental disorder. It is understandable that it can be quite upsetting for a parent to be informed their child has autism/PDD. Under the EIP only a psychologist or physician can make a diagnosis of autism or pervasive developmental disorder-NOS (PDD). However, other evaluators should be able to identify characteristics of autism and PDD and should feel comfortable deciding whether to refer the child for a psychological evaluation. Don't avoid the difficult but important job of referring a child when a pervasive developmental disorder is suspected. In addition, evaluators who are not specifically assessing for autism/PDD can play an important role in the evaluation process. They can write detailed observations of the child that can support the psychologist or physician's observations and diagnosis.

## Steps Involved in Assessing Autism/PDD

There are some important steps in making a diagnosis of autism/PDD. The first step is learning the diagnostic criteria and other background on the disorders. Second, you must obtain detailed information from the parents including using a rating scale designed to assess autism/PDD. Third, make your own observations and engage in activities with the child. Once you have all the information then you can determine whether the child meets the criteria for autism/PDD.

## Diagnostic Criteria

The Early Intervention Program relies on the criteria set by the Diagnostic and Statistical Manual of the American Psychiatric Association IV (DSM IV) to determine diagnoses of autism and pervasive developmental disorder (American Psychiatric Association, 1994). The DSM IV is the fourth edition of a classification system designed by a group of international experts in the fields of psychiatry and mental health. In the DSM IV the pervasive developmental disorders are considered one general category of the Disorders Usually Diagnosed in Infancy, Childhood or Adolescence.

In addition to the DSM IV, there are other diagnostic systems such as the ICD 9, and the 0-3 Diagnostic Classification of Mental Health and Developmental Disorders of Infancy and Early Childhood. The ICD 9 is a classification system developed by the World Health Organization. It is used to classify children for interventions in the Early Intervention Program. The DSM-IV diagnoses have associated ICD 9 codes. The 0-3 Diagnostic Classification System is another system, which was developed by a multidisciplinary task force from the Zero to Three National Center for Clinical Infant Programs. Unlike the DSM IV and the ICD 9, the 0-3 classification system focuses only on infants and young children. It uses a multiaxil framework for diagnosing emotional and developmental problems in early childhood. It attempts to look at the children in the context of their relationships and identifies adaptive strategies as well as developmental difficulties (Zero to Three, 1994).

In the 0-3 Diagnostic Classification System, autism and PDD are classified as difficulties of relating and communicating, multi-system developmental disorder. The diagnostic criteria for multi-system developmental disorder includes significant impairment in the ability to engage in emotional and social relationship with a primary caregiver, significant impairment in forming, maintaining and/or developing communication, significant dysfunction in auditory processing, and significant dysfunction in the processing of other sensations (Zero to Three, 1994). Some researchers suggest that difficulties with sensory integration represent a core deficit of autism (Williamson & Anzalone, 2000). They suggest that the sensory dysfunction may be the core deficit and may underlie the difficulties in relating. Other researchers have noted the lack of specific criteria in the DSM IV for describing children with milder autistic symptoms. They have suggested replacing the classification of PDD with a new more clearly defined diagnosis called mutiplex developmental disorder (Klin, Mayes, Volkmar & Cohen, 1995). This disorder is characterized primarily by disturbances in the modulation of anxiety, impaired social behaviors and peculiarities in thinking. Currently there is much discussion and controversy about how best to describe the behaviors that characterize autism and PDD.

In the DSM IV the term pervasive developmental disorders is used to describe a range of disorders, which are first identified in early childhood. These disorders all involve impairments in communication, social skills and a repertoire of restrictive and repetitive behaviors. These disorders include autism, rett's disorder, childhood disintegrative disorder, asperger's syndrome and pervasive developmental disorder not otherwise specified. Autism is the most well known of these disorders and the term most widely recognized by both parents and professionals. There is often confusion about how to distinguish autism from the other disorders, particularly pervasive developmental disorder-NOS. This chapter will attempt to clarify this issue by describing the characteristics of each disorder as well as other important issues such as the cause, the prevalence, and the prognosis for each one.

## Autism

Children with autistic disorder have significant impairments in the areas of social interaction and communication, as well as displaying restrictive repetitive behaviors. About 75% of autistic children also have significant cognitive delays. There are approximately 2-5 cases of autism per 10,000 births. Symptoms of autism can be detected during the first years of life, usually between the ages of 18 and 30 months. Boys are 3 to 4 times more likely than girls to be affected. Autism in some form often continues its course throughout the life span. However, intensive treatments have been found to produce significant improvements in functioning for a number of children with autism (Seigel, 1996).

Autistic disorder was first described in 1943 by an American child psychiatrist named Leo Kanner. He used the term early infantile autism to describe a group of children who presented with a lack of interest in the world and an inability to relate to others. In the 1950s and 1960s a psychoanalytic theory of autism hypothesized that the autistic child's failure to develop was the result of an unloving relationship with a cold, withdrawn mother Bettelheim (1967). This theory has not been supported by research and is no longer popular.

More recently there is increasing evidence to support the idea that autism is a genetically-based neurological disorder (Bailey, LeCouteur, Gottesman, Bolton, Simionoff, Yuzda, & Rutter, 1995). Studies looking at the characteristics of populations support this notion. For example, the chance of having a child with autism for a family that already has one autistic child is at least one in twenty. When one identical twin has autism there is a 90 percent chance the other will be affected as well. Studies have also found a higher incidence of autism in identical versus fraternal twins (Folstein & Rutter, 1997). Family members of people with autism may also have milder types of impairments including language and social difficulties suggesting that there may be a genetic association (Piven, Arndt, Bailey, Havercamp & Andreasen, 1996). Research has begun to look at the brain development of children with autism. Neuroimaging and autopsy studies have found abnormalities in the cerebellum area as well as other areas of the brain (Askshoomoff, 2000). Other studies have attempted to clarify the role of genetics in the etiology of the role of genetics in the etiology of the role of genetics in the etiology of autism (Rutter, 2000). One study looking at sibling pairs suggested that susceptibility genes for autism are located on chromosome 7 (International Molecular Genetic Study of Autism Consortium, 1998).

Recent reports have indicated a dramatic increase in the rates of autism in areas of the United States. For example, a recent study found a 21% increase in the number of individuals diagnosed with autism in California from 2001 to 2002. (California Department of Developmental Services, 2002). This has led some professionals to suggest a link between autism and the increase of toxins in the environment (Edelson, 2003). Others have hypothesized that the rates of autism have increased due to the more widespread use of vaccines in early childhood to prevent disease (Wakefield, Murch & Anthony, 1998). Research so far has not yet supported this hypothesis. Recently a study of 440,000 children in Denmark who received the MMR vaccine found that vaccine use was not correlated with increased autism rates (Madsen, 2002).

## Rett's Disorder

Rett's disorder is diagnosed only in girls since it results from abnormalities in the X chromosome. Girls develop normally for the first six to eight months of life. By the end of the first year their overall development and head growth slow down. By the end of the second year developmental regression occurs, as well as seizures, hyperventilation and loss of purposeful hand movement. Later the girls develop characteristics of wringing hands, followed by spasticity and frequent loss of ambulation. Girls with rett's disorder are generally mentally retarded and they typically display severely impaired language development, difficulties in social interactions, and stereotyped behaviors. Rett's disorder occurs in 1 in 15,000 births.

## Childhood Disintegrative Disorder

Childhood disintegrative disorder, also known as hellers syndrome, is characterized by marked regression in functioning after a period of at least two years of normal development. Usually the child develops normally for the first two years of life and then at the age of three or four, experiences the loss of previously acquired skills in at least two areas of development including language, social skills, bowel or bladder control, play or motor skills. The child may become mute, may loose the ability to play and develop restrictive, repetitive behaviors. A child with childhood disintegrative disorder is difficult to distinguish from an autistic child and a diagnosis is determined based on the child's developmental history.

The cause of this disorder is unknown. However, it has been associated with seizure disorders. It is thought to result from an injury to the developing nervous system. It is more common among boys although both boys and girls can be affected. Children with this disorder typically continue to display impairments in functioning throughout their life span however the loss of skills usually reaches a plateau.

## Asperger's Syndrome

Asperger's syndrome is considered a milder pervasive developmental disorder and is characterized by impairments in social interaction and restrictive, repetitive behaviors. Children with asperger's syndrome may have difficulty picking up non-verbal social cues and they may have difficulty forming friendships with peers. They may have abnormally intense interests or stick rigidly to routines or rituals. Children with asperger's syndrome usually develop language at the expected time and acquire appropriate grammar and a large vocabulary. However, the content of their speech is abnormal and at times limited to some favorite subjects or copied from other sources. Individuals with asperger's syndrome have no significant cognitive delays or delays in adaptive behavior. Popular writers have referred to this disorder as the "geek syndrome" because of the difficulty with social skills.

An Austrian child psychiatrist named Hans Asperger first identified children with characteristics of this disorder in 1944. These children had some similarities to the children with "Early Infantile Autism" described by Kanner, except that they had language skills. Asperger believed that the disorder was genetically transmitted and he noted that it was more common in families in which fathers had the disorder. Recent research based on neuroimaging studies suggests that it may be associated with brain abnormalities (Ozonoff, Dawson, McParttard, 2002). It has been found to be more common in boys than in girls.

Symptoms of asperger's syndrome often remain in some form throughout the lifespan. The prognosis is variable and related to the level of skill and the particular personality of each individual. Many individuals with asperger's syndrome are able to use their specific skills and interests effectively in a related career. There is some indication that individuals with this disorder are at risk for psychiatric illnesses such as anxiety and depression.

## *Pervasive Developmental Disorder Not Otherwise Specified*

A diagnosis of PDD is given when a child has impairments in the areas of communication, social skills and behavior similar to those described for autism. PDD is different from autism, however in that the child's presentation does not meet the full criteria for autistic disorder. This is due to either late age of onset, atypical or sub threshold symptomatology. For example, a child with PDD may tend to be isolated and hard to engage, like an autistic child, but may make eye contact and initiate some interactions with others. The criteria for this disorder is as follows: "This category should be used when there is a severe and pervasive impairment in the development of reciprocal social interaction or verbal and nonverbal communication skills, or when stereotyped behavior, interests, and activities are present, but the criteria are not met for a specific pervasive developmental disorder, schizophrenia, schizotypal personality disorder or avoidant personality disorder." (DSM IV 1994, p 78).

## *Differential Diagnoses*

Making a diagnosis of autism or one of the pervasive developmental disorders involves differentiating or distinguishing the disorder from other childhood disorders. This process is called differential diagnosis. There are several common groups of disorders from which a diagnosis of autism/PDD must be differentiated: communication disorders, mental retardation or overall developmental delays, and behavioral disorders (e.g., attention-deficit/hyperactivity disorder). Differentiating autism from communication disorders, mental retardation (overall delays), and behavioral disorders is mainly done by observing the child's interpersonal relatedness, and emotional responsiveness. When a child has one of the other disorders there will still be an ability to relate to others. He may display some problematic social interactions such as aggressive behavior or attentional difficulties, however he still shows an interest in others and can respond to others appropiately. Children diagnosed with autism/PDD may make eye contact, but perhaps only intermittently. If there is eye contact they may seem to look through you, and they may not look at you to check out your reactions. They do not seem to relate to you emotionally in an appropriate way. For

133

example, they may not respond when you praise them or smile at them. They may come near you, but not get involved in an activity with you such as reading. They tend to wander off and act like they are "in their own world."

## The Parent Interview

It is natural for parents to feel anxious when their child is being seen for any developmental evaluation. However, their anxiety if usually more intense if they are concerned that their child may have a pervasive developmental disorder or autism. Do your best to calm the parents by answering their questions, trying to understand their child as thoroughly as possible with their help, and giving them feedback about your impressions at the end of the session.

We recommend that you begin the parent interview by asking your own set of questions. Then with the information obtained you can complete one of the autism rating scales. Detailed information obtained from your parent interview will be critical in assessing the child. Refer to Chapter 5 for suggestions on your interviewing and questioning style. Use a variety of question types to obtain the most complete information you can from the parent. If you use general questions, make sure you follow up with specific questions. You will want to understand exactly what kind of behaviors the child displays. In addition you will need to know the frequency, intensity, duration and context of the behaviors.

To assist you in examining a child's behavior when there is a suspicion of autism or PDD, we have developed a list of questions to guide the parent interview. You do not have to ask the parent every question in the interview guide. If you ask a few questions and determine that there is little concern about one area of development, then you do not need to continue asking questions about that area. If the parent mentions something that is not addressed in the interview guide, follow up with some additional questions of your own.

# Early Childhood Autism/ Pervasive Developmental Disorder Assessment Guide (ECAAG)

*Directions*: This assessment guide was developed to assist in the identification and diagnosis of young children with Autism and Pervasive Developmental Disorder-NOS. Use this guide to focus your questions to parents/caretakers and to organize your observations. With detailed information obtained from this guide, and from a complete assessment of the child, an appropriate decision can be made as to whether or not a child meets the diagnostic criteria for Autism or Pervasive Developmental Disorder. Use this guide to assist both with the **parent interview**, as well as the **observations**. The first question in each topic area is general, and the rest of the questions are more specific. If the general questions is answered **yes**, this indicates that no difficulties are noted in that topic area. Answers of **no** to the general question indicate there is a difficulty that may indicate Autism or PDD. Further questioning is then needed. Use this guide as an outline of suggested questions to assist in structuring your interview and observations. You need not ask all questions. These questions are intended to be followed by more detailed follow up to obtain more information about the description, frequency, intensity, duration, and context of the behaviors reported. Note that the responses to each question are only meaningful only when the child's age is taken into account. For example, very limited vocabulary of a few words is considered "normal" for a one-year-old, but not typical of a three-year-old.

# I. COMMUNICATION

## 1. VOCALIZATIONS, JARGON

*Is the child expressing him/herself with vocalizations appropriately for his/her age?*
Does the child say vowel consonant combinations such as "mamama" or "bababa"?
Does the child sound like he/she is trying to say words (word attempts)?
What do the vocalizations/jargon sound like?
Are the child's sounds age appropriate?
Does the child frequently make any odd, unusual sounds or squeals?

## 2. EXPRESSIVE VOCABULARY

*Does the child have an age-appropriate vocabulary?*
Does the child use any words with meaning?
How many words does the child use spontaneously with meaning?
Does the child repeat words said by others without understanding their meaning (echoing, parrotting)?
Does the child use any words to express his needs?
Does the child say the names of any familiar objects or foods?
Does he/she use the names of familiar people?
Does the child use word combinations, such as "mama bye bye" or "more juice"?

## 3. DEVELOPMENTAL PROGRESSION OF LANGUAGE

*Is the child steadily developing language skills without any language regression?*
Are there some words the child used to say when he/she was younger but can no longer say?
Are there some words the child said once or twice but has not repeated again?

## 4. IMITATING SOUNDS, WORDS AND ACTIONS

*Is the child imitating sounds, words or actions appropriately for his/her age?*
Does the child imitate sounds?
Does the child imitate words?
Does the child imitate the actions of other people or TV characters?

## 5. NONVERBAL COMMUNICATION

***Does the child use gestures (including pointing) to express him/herself and his/her needs?***

Does the child point to what he/she wants?

Can the child choose which of two objects he/she wants by pointing?

Does the child shake his/her head to indicate yes or no?

Does the child frequently pull you by the hand to show you what he/she wants, rather than pointing to it?

Does the child imitate gestures such as clapping or waving goodbye?

Does the child try to communicate with gestures?

## 6. LANGUAGE COMPREHENSION

***Is the child understanding as many words and phrases as expected for his/her age?***

Does the child understand his/her name?

How many objects can the child identify?

Can the child respond to simple verbal requests (e.g., "bring me your shoes") when the object is out of sight, and without pointing or using gestures?

How many verbs does the child seem to understand?

## II. SOCIAL-EMOTIONAL

### 7. EYE CONTACT

***Does the child make regular and appropriate eye contact?***

Does the child make regular eye contact with you or other familiar people?

When the child is in a new or challenging situation does the child check in with you for reassurance by making eye contact?

Does the child avoid looking at others or look at others only if persistent attempts are made to engage him/her?

### 8. RELATEDNESS

***Does the child show an interest in other people and interact appropriately with others?***

Does the child show interest in joining in the activities of others?

Does the child display joint attention (the ability to join others in attending to a common activity)?

How often does the child initiate interactions with others?

How much will the child respond positively when others interact with him/her?

When other children approach the child, does the child interact or tend to back away?

Does the child seem to be "in his/her own world," and show little interest in others?

Does the child only show interest in running and chasing other children, or does
the child interact in a variety of ways with other children?
How does the child express his/her needs?
Does the child show desire to interact beyond expressing his/her needs?
Does he/she demonstrate an awareness of other peoples interests, needs, feelings?

## 9. AFFECTION

***Does the child give and receive affection appropriately?***
Does the child accept affection from others?
Will the child hug and kiss when asked to do so?
Will the child hug or kiss in responses to affection from others?
Will the child hug and kiss you and other family members spontaneously?

## 10. EMOTIONAL RESPONSES

***Is the type and degree of the child's emotional response appropriate to a given
situation?***
Does the child seem happy when complimented or praised?
Does the child laugh for no apparent reason?
Does the child seem overly serious, or underreactive to situations?
Does the child act overly upset when you tell him/her "no"?
Does the child cry excessively?
Does the child become frustrated too easily?
How often does he/she tantrum, how long do they last, and how does the child
calm down?
Does he/she often become overly upset?
How often does he/she become overly aggressive (e.g., hit, kick, bite, throw
things)?
Does the child show aggression towards him/herself (e.g., hitting self, headbanging)?

## 11. TRANSITIONING

***Will the child accept changes in routine or activities without much difficulty, to
the extent appropriate for his/her age?***
Does the child become very upset when it is time to leave the house to go outside?
Does the child become overly upset when it is time to come home?
Does the child become very upset when it is time to take a bath, have dinner, or go
to sleep?
Does the child become very upset (e.g., tantrums, screams), when you say it is time
to stop one activity and move to another activity?

## 12. ACTIVITY LEVEL

*Is the child appropriately active for his/her age?*
Is the child extremely active compared to other children his/her age?
Does the child appear lethargic or move very slowly compared to other children his/her age?

## 13. FEAR

*Does the child show fear appropriate to a given situation?*
Is the child appropriately scared of unfamiliar, large animals, loud noises or the dark?
Is the child overly fearful of familiar people, animals or bugs?
Does the child seem unaware of danger (e.g. climbing on high furniture, running out into the street without being fearful of cars)?

# III. ATYPICAL BEHAVIORS

## 14. BEHAVIORS OF CONCERN

*Is the child free of the following?*
Hand flapping, toe walking, finger wiggling, hitting or covering ears, hitting self, grimacing, unusual body posturing, spinning, rocking?
Are there any other unusual behaviors you have noticed or are concerned about?

# IV. SENSORY ISSUES

## 15. VISUAL PROCESSING

*Does the child look appropriately at objects?*
Does the child like to stare at spinning objects such as a ceiling fan or the wheels on a toy?
Does the child stare at lights?
Does the child stare at his reflection in the mirror?
Does the child stare into space?

## 16. AUDITORY PROCESSING

*Does the child react normally to sound without over or underreacting?*
Is the child demonstrating any unusual reactions to sounds?
Is the child very sensitive to noise? For example, does the child seem afraid of the
    vacuum cleaner, blender, or the sound of a loud passing truck?
Does the child seem unaware of loud noises?
Does the child seem not to notice when you turn on the vacuum cleaner or the
    blender?
Do you wonder if the child can hear properly because he/she ignores you fre-
    quently?

## 17. TACTILE PROCESSING

*Does the child show appropriate tactile responses?*
Does the child dislike certain textures, or substances?
Does the child mind the tags on clothing?
Does the child mind crèmes or oils on his/her body?
Does the child refuse to wear certain items of clothing because they feel uncom-
    fortable?
Does the child hate to touch dirt or sand with his/her hands or feet?
Does the child hate to get his/her hands dirty?
Does the child over or underreact to painful sensations?
Does the child seem overly interested in playing or splashing with water?

## 18. VESTIBULAR PROCESSING

*Does the child moves with his/her body appropriately?*
Does the child repeatedly spin him/herself around?
Does the child like to spin around?
Does the child like to rock back and forth?
Does the child flap his hands when excited?

## 19. ORAL AND OLFACTORY PROCESSING

*Does the child taste and smell foods and other objects appropriately?*
Does the child smell things that don't smell, such as plastic toys?
Does the child lick or chew on inedible food or objects such as plastic toys?
Is the child frequently putting toys or objects in his/her mouth, and more than
    expected at his/her age?
Does the child eat a variety of foods and textures?

## 20. MOTOR COORDINATION

*Does the child show age-appropriate motor coordination?*
Does the child wobble or seem insecure when he/she walks?
Does the child stumble or fall frequently when running?
Does the child have difficulty grasping small objects in his/her hands?
Does the child have difficulty stacking blocks or putting pieces into a puzzle?

# V. COGNITIVE

## 21. COGNITIVE FUNCTIONING

*Are the child's cognitive skills at age level?*
Does the child know as much as expected at his/her age?
Is the child showing problem solving abilities at age level?

## 22. EVENNESS OF COGNITIVE SKILLS

*Is the child developing cognitive skills relatively evenly?*
Does the child only say a few words, but counts, knows the letters of the alphabet, or has other unexpectedly strong skills?

## 23. ATTENTION SPAN

*Does the child display an age appropriate attention span?*
Is the child able to focus for an appropriate amount of time on a play activity?
Does the child sit and listen when you read him/her a story?
Does the child play for an excessive amount of time with one favorite toy?
Does the child seem to loose interest in activities too quickly?
Does the child wander aimlessly?

## 24. PLAY ACTIVITIES AND SKILLS

*Does the child show age appropriate play skills?*
Does the child play with toys/objects appropriately (e.g., building with blocks instead of throwing them)?
Does the child focus on only one part of a toy?
Does the child like to play with the same toy over and over again rather than playing with new toys?
Does the child frequently stack or line up objects?
Does the child become upset if someone disrupts the lines of toys he/she has made?
Does the child engage in imaginative play (e.g. pretending to feed a baby doll, pretending to talk to someone on the phone)?

## Using Rating Scales and Other Assessment Measures

According to the DSM-IV diagnostic criteria, children with autism and PDD present with qualitative impairments in social interaction, communication and restricted, repetitive patterns of behavior. A variety of assessment tools have been developed to help establish whether a child meets the criteria for autism or PDD. A good resource to learn more about these scales is the New York State Clinical Practice Guideline for autism/pervasive developmental disorders (2000). Keep in mind that a rating scale is only an aide in diagnosis. The evaluator must make the final determination of a diagnosis based on all the information available. It is possible, for example, that a child does not score in the autistic spectrum on a rating scale, but qualifies for a diagnosis of pervasive developmental disorder based on the evaluator's observations and the parent report. The following are rating scales and interviews that can help in the assessment of autism and PDD:

**Childhood Autism Rating Scale—CARS** (Schopler, Reichler, DeVellis, & Daly, 1980). This scale is one of the most concise and it has high reliability and validity. For these reasons the New York State panel that produced the Guidelines (2000) has recommended use of this scale. It is composed of fifteen items, each rated from one to four. Children receive a score of 15 -60 with 15 to 29.5 representing the Non-Autistic range, 30 – 36.5 representing the Mildly-Moderately Autistic range, and more than 37 representing the Severely Autistic range.

**Checklist for Autism in Toddlers–CHAT** (Baron-Cohen, 1992). This scale is used to screen for autism at 18 months of age. It is comprised of a short questionnaire. One section is completed by parents (9 questions), and the other by the child's pediatrician or health visitor (5 items). This has not yet been shown to have a high level of predictive value upon follow up (Baron-Cohen, Wheelwright, Cox, Baird, Charman, Swettenham, Drew, & Doehring, 2000).

**Autism Diagnostic Interview-Revised—ADI** (Lord, Rutter, & LeCouteur, 1994). This interview contains a large number of questions about the child's past and present behavior. Each response is scored and the total score indicates whether the child meets the criteria for autism. This is a lengthy measure and is used primarily for research studies.

***Autism Behavior Checklist—ABC*** (Krug, Arick, & Almond, 1978, 1980). This measure includes 57 statements. Parents are asked to circle those statements which most accurately describe their child. Most of the items are easy to understand, easy to rate, and are relevant for young children.

## Informal Assessment and Behavior Observations

Children with autism and related disorders often present with a pattern of behaviors which can be identified at a very early age. Clinician who are observant and ask the appropriate questions to parents will often be able to identify these patterns. It is important to check in with the parents regularly to ask the parents if the behaviors you are observing in the child are typical. If the child is friendly and sociable during the observation, ask the parent if this is how he usually is. If the child displays odd behaviors, ask if those behaviors are typical. Don't wait until the end of the interview to first ask about whether the child was behaving typically. When you are evaluating for autism or PDD, you need to be even more detailed in your observations of the child's behavior, and you need to check in more often with the parent, so you can determine the extent to which the child's behavior is typical.

## Important Issues in Assessing the Pervasive Developmental Disorders

It is a challenging and complex process for evaluators to determine whether a young child presents with autism or PDD. This needs to be done cautiously as each child presents with their own set of behaviors, their own personalities and idiosyncrasies. For example, some children with difficulties in reciprocal social interaction still make regular eye contact and display affection toward their parents. Other children may have impaired language and social skills but may not display the repetitive motor mannerisms often associated with autism, such as hand flapping, finger wiggling or toe walking. Because of the complexity of each child's presentation, evaluators must look for a pattern of functioning that fits the criteria for autism or PDD. It is not a simple process of adding up behaviors from a checklist to make a diagnosis.

It is important to identify areas of strength when evaluating young children. This may seem challenging when working with autistic children, particularly if they have significant delays in language and social skills. Some autistic children may have limited verbal skills and may communicate more easily through drawing or movement. They may have a capacity for relatedness even though this may only be demonstrated with very familiar people or on their own terms. Some autistic children may have isolated cognitive skills such as the ability to remember letters, numbers, songs, or to remember dialogue from a movie or television show. Some may have abilities in the area of perceptual-motor skills, and can, for example, complete puzzles beyond age expectations.

## Discussing the Pervasive Developmental Disorders with Parents

One of the most difficult things to tell parents is that their child has autism or PDD. Parents are naturally concerned about this diagnosis. Try to be sensitive to how upsetting this can be. Your objective should be to provide some brief, but meaningful feedback, and encourage the parents to discuss your report more thoroughly with you when they have received it. Be cautious not to provide too much information before reviewing your findings and writing your report. This is not advised for several reasons. First, since you have not reviewed all your findings, you might end up contradicting yourself later on in your report. Second, the parents may naturally feel overwhelmed at the end of the evaluation, and may not be ready to hear extensive feedback. Third, the parents should be given a little time to think about the general information, before having to see the details of your report. To avoid causing the parents undo stress, it is best to complete your report quickly so it can be sent to the parents in a timely fashion.

In giving feedback about autism, be aware of the possible emotional impact of your statements on the family and be prepared for a variety of reactions. Some parents may be very shocked, or sad. Others may be angry or resentful. Still others may seem to accept your findings fairly easily, or even feel relieved that you have validated their concerns. Feedback should be tailored to the parents' level of education, level of understanding, and readiness to learn about the diagnosis.

The following are some tips to remember when giving feedback to parents.

**FOCUS ON**
Strengths
Specific, observable behaviors
Parent concerns
Common ground with parents
Supporting parent observations
Next steps

**AVOID**
Interpretations
Definitive Diagnosis
(until the report is complete)
Definitive Prognosis

# Autism/Pervasive Developmental Disorder Symptom Checklist

## Communication Difficulties
O Limited/odd/atypical vocalizations
O Very limited vocabulary
O Excessive jargon
O Echolalia (parroting)
O Difficulty expressing needs
O Pulls people to what he/she wants
   instead of pointing or talking
O Little or no pointing
O Limited nonverbal communication
O Unresponsive to own name
O Unresponsive to simple requests asked once
O Does not understand/respond to simple words
O Little or no imitation

## Social Skills Delays
O Lack of, or minimal, eye contact
O Limited relatedness with others
O Limited joint attention
O Lack of interest in people
O Prefers to play alone with things instead of people
O Affect changes rapidly, inappropriately
O Easily frustrated and upset
O Gets upset or laughs for no apparent reason
O Frequent tantrums
O Difficulty transitioning from one activity to the next
O Only communicates needs,
   does not comment on things or people

## Cognitive Delays
O Significant cognitive delay
O Uneven cognitive skills
O Short attention span
O Delayed play skils
O Wanders aimlessly

## Atypical Behaviors
O Hand flapping
O Toe walking
O Finger wiggling
O Lines up objects
O Hits or covers ears or head
O Hits self
O Repetitive play

## Sensory Integration Difficulties
O Spins self or objects
   (e.g., wheels on toy cars)
O Stares at lights, fans, or spinning objects
O Feels, smells or tastes objects too much
O Dislikes certain textures, substances
   (e.g. dirty hands, tags on clothes, grass, sand)
O Resists being held or cuddled
O Hypersensitive or insensitive to loud sounds
O Poor coordination, clumsy, falls frequently
O Puts toys or other objects in mouth constantly
O Odd body posturing

Instructions: These symptoms are noted in children diagnosed with Autistic Disorder, and Pervasive Developmental Disorder-NOS. Use this checklist as a guide to assist in identifying these disorders. Note that any "symptoms" need to be carefully considered in a developmental context, and may not be "symptoms" depending on the age of the child. For example, "very limited vocabulary" is normal for a child under 18 months of age. This list can help organize observations and inform the overall assessment of a child's development and possible diagnosis. Use this checklist as part of a complete assessment in which other diagnostic tools are included such as rating scales.

*X.*

# *Writing Early Intervention Reports*

This chapter will focus on the actual writing of the evaluation report. If you have been successful at engaging the family and the child, and have completed all aspects of the evaluation, then the task of writing the report will be easier. Even when the evaluation goes well up to this point, the final challenge is to write a report that captures the child as fully as possible and is accepted by the parents and the other professionals who will use the report to plan for any indicated services. In this chapter we will provide a sample outline of an evaluation report and describe the issues faced in each section. We will also identify some common report-writing problems and offer practical solutions.

## *Purpose of the reports*

Early Intervention reports serve two main purposes: describing the child's functioning and determining whether a child is eligible for Early Intervention services. In describing the child's functioning, it is important to give a clear picture of what the child is doing at this time, what the child is not yet doing, and any problem areas. Reports should provide clear examples of the child's behaviors, including descriptions of how the child performs on the specific tasks that make up the formal evaluation. Providing specific examples of the child's behavior helps to support the evaluators' overall impressions of the child's functioning. An effective report will also clearly state whether or not the child meets the eligibility criteria for Early Intervention services. This will be based on the child's scores on the formal testing measures, as well as on the evaluator's professional opinion and impressions of the child's level of functioning.

## Analyzing the Results

Effective reports integrate all the sources of information about the child, including the parent interview, the formal assessment and the informal assessment. Each of these components should be analyzed and compared with one other in order to get a full picture of the child. Sometimes, information from one source will not be in complete agreement with information from another source. In that case, you will have to try to make sense of all the information. For example, a child may be attentive and cooperative during the evaluation, but the parent may report that the child is usually overactive and uncooperative at home. You must make sense of this apparent discrepancy. Could it be that the child responds better to the structure of the formal evaluation, and that in unstructured situations, or when he is not being given as much one-to-one attention from an adult, he becomes restless? Was the child particularly attentive because of the novelty of the evaluation activities? The evaluator may have to entertain many hypotheses before choosing the one that seems to fit best with all the available information about the child. There is no simple method for analyzing the results. Instead, you are encouraged to review all of the material, to look for consistencies and inconsistencies, and then to do your best to make sense of the child. When you are highly successful in integrating your findings, parents will read the report and say something to the effect of "That's my child. You described him exactly." Learning how to analyze your findings well is best done under supervision from an experienced evaluation supervisor who can review your reports and provide feedback to you. If possible, we also recommend having your supervisor observe your evaluation session, either in person or on videotape, and then reviewing your work, and your written report, with you.

## Confidentiality and Dealing with Sensitive Information

When you work with parents, you want them to feel comfortable enough to give you all needed information. Sometimes, parents will feel so comfortable with you that they will reveal very confidential and sensitive details. They will entrust you with this information and may not think about if, or how, you are going to record what they have said in your written report. Use your judgment about what to include. You need not include all information just because you discussed it with the parent. For example, you do not need to include specific information about the parents employers or their workplace locations. The best advice is to try to be sensitive during the evaluation itself and to check in with the parent if you think they may not want certain information in the report. We have had the experience of writing what we thought was a sensitively written report—but then upsetting parents who felt that information that was too personal was included. Remember that sensitive information and confidentiality go hand in hand. Your evaluation report is confidential and only to be submitted to the evaluation agency. It can only be shared with Early Intervention professionals involved in the case or with other people (such as the child's pediatrician) who have written consent from the parents. Some parents are naturally concerned about confidentiality. Thus, do not include any unnecessary, personally identifying information.

## HIV/AIDS Information

Check your locality to determine if any information about AIDS or HIV status is permitted at all. The best rule is not to include information about AIDS or HIV status—of the child or anyone else.

# Suggested Outline for Evaluation Report

## Identifying Information
Child's name
Informants' names
Child's date of birth
Date of evaluation
Age
Name of evaluation agency
Languages used in the home
Languages used in the evaluation
Names of interviews and measures used in the evaluation

## Reason for Referral
Who referred the child
Reason for evaluation
Parents' response to referral

## Concerns, Priorities, and Resources (CPR)
All parents' concerns
Concerns that are priorities to the parents
Parents' financial resources
Important social supports
Transportation needs

## Background Information
Family background
Living situation
Family configuration
Parents' country of origin
Parents' immigration status
Languages to which child is exposed
Parents' schooling
Parents' employment
Child-care arrangements
Foster care
Domestic violence
Substance abuse
Legal issues
Development
Prenatal care
Pregnancy and birth

Birth weight
Illnesses/Medical conditions
Hospitalizations
Medications
Developmental milestones

## Behavioral Observations
Attention
Activity level
Affect
Aggressive behavior
Concentration
Cooperation
Eye contact
Frustration tolerance
Mood
Relatedness
Tantrums
Temperament
Transitioning

## Statement of Validity
Are results of testing a valid estimate of child's optimal functioning?

## Findings
Bilingual disclaimer (if appropriate)
Scores in each area of development
Did child perform above, at or below age level in each area?
Is child eligible for services in each area of development?
Describe child's functioning in each area

## Summary
Strengths and notable behaviors
Is child developmentally advanced, at, or below age level?
Is the child eligible for services?
Were the parents informed of the evaluator's impressions and
     recommendations?
Child's diagnosis

## Recommendations
Recommendations for additional evaluations (e.g. speech, occupational
     therapy, physical therapy, audiological, psychiatry, psychological, social
     work, feeling evaluations)
Recommendations for services

## Report Writing Issues

### Identifying Information

When writing the identifying information, be sure to check the spelling of all names. Parents will naturally feel upset if they see that their child's name is spelled incorrectly throughout the evaluation. Pay special attention to verifying the date of birth, as this is essential for all your calculations regarding the child's level of development.

### Reason for Referral

In this section include whether or not the parents' agreed with the referral. Usually they do agree with the need for the referral and, in fact, many parents themselves initiate the referral process. Sometimes parents have no concerns of their own but agree to go along with a referral initiated by a professional (usually the child's pediatrician). State what the parents say is the reason for the referral. For example, you might state that the parent reported that the pediatrician recommended the evaluation because of concern that the child is not yet walking. Avoid comments like, "The pediatrician referred the child because..." You don't know exactly what the pediatrician said to the parent, and you will be more accurate to state what "the parent reported that the child's pediatrician referred the child for evaluation due to concern about..."

### Concerns, Priorities and Resources (CPR)

Indicate all of the parents concerns, their priorities, and any resources they have, related to assisting the child (e.g., they may need transportation assistance for any needed appointments). You may explore social support.

### Background Information

Describe the child's family background and developmental and medical history in this section of the report. Be particularly cautious when discussing sensitive personal information, such as substance abuse, domestic violence, and medical and psychiatric issues. As stated above, the parents may feel very comfortable speaking to you and telling you about these matters. However, they may not intend for this information to be written in the report.

152

When reporting personal information, some parents have complained when the evaluator writes that the parent "denies" substance abuse or domestic violence. Some parents think that the use of the word "deny" or "denies" insinuates that the parents may have engaged in the behavior but do not want to admit it. It is better to write something along the lines of "The parent states that there is no drug or alcohol abuse in their family."

Sometimes the details of important issues are not known (e.g., the name of a child's medical condition). If the parent is unclear about some specifics, then report what they say. In the case of the child's medical condition, describe it as fully as possible—you can consult the pediatrician for details.

At times, a parent may not appear to be a reliable informant and may give vague or apparently contradictory information about the child's behavior. Do not make comments in the report that are critical of the parent or, worse yet, insulting. For example, you might state that the parent "was not exactly sure when the child began to walk, but believes it was when the child was approximately between 10 and 12 months of age." But do not write that "the parent was an unreliable informant."

### *Behavioral Observations*

Use as much detail as you can in the behavioral observations to paint a picture of the child. Your readers should feel that they can visualize the child and what happened during the evaluation. It is alright to include general kinds of words and observations, such as "The child had a short attention span," but back up general statements with specifics: "He left the testing area more than 10 times during the hour long session, and was only able to focus on tasks for 1 – 2 minutes at a time." Describe the child with as much detail as needed to help the reader fully understand the child's behavior.

It is best to avoid judgmental adjectives, such as "cute," "sweet," and "adorable." Instead, use positive but more objective adjectives: "curious," "engaging," "friendly." Be sensitive when describing the child's physical characteristics. Such terms as "Mongoloid features" should be avoided. When noting behaviors, it can help to mention the frequency, duration, intensity, and context of the behavior. This will help the reader to visualize the child. These descriptions do not have to be long; for example, you can say the child "got frustrated when the examiner asked for the blocks back and offered a puzzle board instead. The child had a tantrum on the floor, kicking and screaming for a few minutes, but then recovered on his own, and went on to complete the testing."

Your description of the child should not come as a surprise to the parents. It should reflect what occurred, and indicate if this is typical of the child. When you describe the child well the parents will make comments such as "you described my child perfectly," or "that's him."

### Statement of Validity

Before discussing the findings, it is helpful to include a statement regarding the validity of the evaluation. This statement tells the reader if the parents believed that the child was performing in a typical manner during the evaluation and if the evaluation results are determined to represent a valid and optimal estimate of the child's functioning. If the findings are not considered to be valid, you need to rectify this, likely by re-evaluating the child on another occasion.

### Findings

Most assessment measures are not standardized for bilingual populations. If an evaluator is working with a bilingual child but using a measure that is not standardized for bilingual children, it is important to include a disclaimer in the evaluation report. A good place to put this disclaimer is at the beginning of the findings section of the report. It should state that the standardized measure was not normed on a bilingual population, and therefore only a range of scores should be considered when evaluating the child's performance. An example of a bilingual disclaimer is as follows:

> "Daniel is from a bilingual/bicultural environment. Thus, only ranges, rather than individual scores, will be reported. This is consistent with recommendations for limited English proficiency and bilingual children. Results should be considered estimates of ability and interpreted with caution, due to the absence of appropriate local norms and deviation from standard procedures to accommodate bilingual issues."

Findings will likely make up the main section of the report. There are many ways to convey findings. Our suggestion is to clearly identify each area that you assess. For developmental evaluations, we suggest dividing the findings section of your report into the five areas of development: communication, cognitive, adaptive, motor, and social. It is helpful in the findings section to integrate the results of the parent interview, the formal assessment, and the informal assessment. You should include test scores and/or ranges of functioning from the evaluation measures, as well as statements about whether the child performed above, at, or below age level. Also state whether or not the child was eligible for services in each area of development. Alternatively, put the test report detail in the body of your report and add a "test score addendum" at the end of the report. For psychological evaluations, you may want to address areas besides the 5 domains of functioning and thus you may wish to provde more subheadings in the findings section. You can vary your subheadings based on the referral reason, and the areas of concern for that particular child. For example, you may wish to include a section on sensory issues or imitation.

An effectively written report will include enough detail to enable a reader to understand how the child is functioning in any given area. It will reveal what the child is currently doing in the area and what the child is not yet doing. Be careful to only include issues that are relevant for the child's age. For example, say that you are evaluating an infant who is 6 months old. In the motor section of the report, you need not state that the child is not walking. If you include irrelevant information, which is only appropriate for older children, then readers will react by saying, "Of course the baby is not walking. The baby is only 6 months old." Children are not expected to walk until a bit before or after they are a year old. Including information that is irrelevant will often lead readers to question the rest of your report.

### Summary

A summary should include key findings from the evaluation. It should be brief but comprehensive. The summary should include strengths as well as need areas for the child. It should include your understanding of how the child is developing in general, a diagnosis (if indicated), and whether you discussed the findings with the parent.

## Recommendations

Evaluation reports are most helpful to parents, and most readily accepted by EI personnel, when they recommend a general type of intervention, as opposed to a specific program. This allows for a range of service options, depending on the needs and interests of the child and family, and on the availability of services. For example, if one desirable early childhood program is full, the family can consider the possibility of meeting the child's needs in another way, with another program, or with therapists in the home. This allows the personnel involved in the IFSP meeting more freedom to decide what is best for the child after reading all of the evaluation reports. If one evaluator has been overly specific in his/her recommendations, this will reduce the flexibility of the IFSP team members in designing an intervention plan. At the IFSP meeting, a team of professionals, along with the child's family, will discuss the evaluation reports and the needs of the child and family to determine which specific programs or services will be most appropriate. Services will be approved based on issues such as the child's needs, the availability of programs, convenience for the family, and the family's interest.

You should only recommend therapeutic goals in your area of expertise. For example, the speech evaluator should offer speech goals, the physical therapist should provide gross-motor goals, and so on. An appropriate recommendation for a child with significant cognitive and social delays might state, for example, "Consider enrolling in an appropriate early childhood program to facilitate overall development and to increase social skills." An example of an overly specific recommendation would be to "enroll the child in a developmental group 5 days per week, 2.5 hours/day." Avoid recommendations which include frequency, type and duration of services.

The regulations for report writing will vary depending on your locality. We are aware of some localities that do not want recommendations included at all in the reports. These localities prefer to develop their own intervention plans, based purely on the report results. Check with your locality to determine how recommendations should be handled.

Evaluators can recommend additional evaluations in areas of development besides their own. For example, when performing a developmental evaluation, you may notice that the child is not communicating as well as expected for his age. You should then refer for a speech evaluation, with the parents' consent.

The recommendations are the "bottom line" of the report. They must address the parents' concerns that you indicated in the beginning of the report. If not, you will have not addressed the original reasons for the evaluation.

## Common Report Writing Problems and Solutions

In our experience with writing and supervising evaluation reports, we have found that certain types of report writing problems often arise. By providing concrete solutions to these problems, we hope to make the writing process easier and more efficient for evaluators. The following is a list of what we have found to be the six most common report writing problems.

*Unclear determination of eligibility*: Evaluators do not clearly indicate why they believe the child is eligible for services, and/or do not back up their determination with the appropriate supporting information such as important scores, percentiles, or rationale for the professional opinion. Thus, the reader cannot determine if the child is eligible for services, or not.

*Unclear, insufficient, or inappropriate recommendations:* Evaluators do not make recommendations that are easily understandable to parents and other professionals and which address all of the concerns regarding the child's functioning.

*Inconsistencies in the report and among evaluators:* Inconsistencies exist within different sections of the evaluation report or your report is inconsistent with the findings of another evaluator.

*Disorganization*: Reports are difficult to read because they lack a clear organizational structure.

*Not parent-friendly*: Reports do not adequately address parent concerns and are not written so that they are clear, free of technical jargon, and sensitive to the parents' feelings or to cultural issues.

**Inconsistent with EI regulations**: Reports do not meet the most recent EI regulations.

## Determining Eligibility

Evaluation reports must clearly state whether or not a child qualifies for Early Intervention services. A child may qualify based on his scores on the formal testing measures or based on the evaluator's professional judgment. The evaluation report should clearly state whether the determination of eligibility is based on the scores, professional judgment, or a combination of both. In addition, if the child is performing below age level based on his performance on formal measures, the specific amount of delay must be stated in terms of a percent or standard deviation (see chapter 2 for details). A child may also automatically qualify for services if he has a diagnosed physical or medical condition (see chapter 2). A child may qualify for services using professional opinion. It is not sufficient to state that the examiner is using professional opinion. The professional opinion, rather than, or in addition to, formal test findings, must still be presented in relation to the criteria for eligibility.

## Writing Clear and Appropriate Recommendations

Issues involved in writing recommendations are detailed above. By writing clear and appropriate recommendations, you help the child to obtain the services he needs to increase his development.

## Being Consistent

Reports will only be understandable and persuasive to the reader if they are consistent throughout the different sections of the report. This means that statements made in one section of the report should be supported by statements made in other sections. In particular, any referral issues or parental concerns introduced in the referral section of the report should be addressed in the findings section, the summary, and the recommendations section. For example, if a pediatrician is concerned about a child's speech, this should be mentioned in the referral section, discussed further in the findings, and reviewed in the summary, and appropriate recommendations should be made. A speech evaluation should also be recommended.

Sometimes parents express several concerns. Address all of their concerns in the report, not only the primary concern. For example, a parent may be most concerned about her child's language development. However, she may also mention that her child has difficulty sleeping. Although evaluators may address the language difficulties, they might ignore the child's sleep problem. Be consistent throughout the report. If a concern about sleep is mentioned in the referral section, be sure to address your findings about this issue and your recommendations about how to address it.

Consistency is also important in your use of language. A report also will be more clear and coherent if you stick to the same tense throughout. Often the past tense is the appropriate tense to use to describe the child's behaviors on the day of the evaluation. For example, the child "built a tower of six blocks, completed a nine-piece puzzle, and copied a horizontal line." The present tense can be used if the evaluator wants to make a generalization about the child's level of functioning. For example, ". . . therefore, the child is estimated to be performing below age level in social skills."

Consistency among the different evaluation reports helps to present a clear and coherent picture of the child. One way to ensure consistency among reports is for each evaluator to stick to his or her area of expertise. This is particularly important for special educators or psychologists who cover multiple areas of development in their core evaluations. It helps to be brief and specific when discussing areas of development that will be evaluated further by another professional. You should consult with other professionals evaluating the child to address any potential inconsistencies.

## Creating an Organized Report

An organized report begins with clear headings for each area covered. This will make it easier for parents and other professionals to follow the organization of the report and to identify the different areas of development being addressed. An organized evaluation report also clearly differentiates parental reports of the child's typical behavior from the evaluator's observations. If the evaluator writes, for example, "The child can clap his hands and wave goodbye," the reader will not know if the parents reported this or if the child actually performed these

159

behaviors on the day of the evaluation. Even though the parents report and the evaluator's observations are often similar, it is still important to distinguish between the two. The parents will want to see that you captured their comments accurately. If the report has even small inaccuracies, the parents may then question your findings and recommendations.

## Writing in a Parent-Friendly Manner

Reports are more understandable and more acceptable to parents if they are written in a parent-friendly manner. They can be parent-friendly in several ways. For example, they should clearly address parents' concerns. Sometimes a concern presented by a parent may not appear to be problematic to you as the evaluator. Nevertheless, to be responsive, you must address the issue. For example, one mother worried that her child would not eat the soups she prepared for dinner. Although the evaluator thought the child appeared healthy and saw him eating other nutritious foods, she did a thorough interview with the mother in order to better understand the child's eating habits, in case additional interventions or evaluations were necessary, such as a feeding evaluation.

Strive to avoid jargon. By using straightforward, down-to-earth language, your reports will be understood by all readers. If you feel technical terms will enhance the report, be sure to explain what they mean. Overall, we have found that the less technical language used, the better.

A parent-friendly report also emphasizes a child's strengths. One way to do this is to begin each section of the report by describing what tasks the child attempted or completed successfully during the evaluation, and what the parent reports the child can do, before describing what the child did not do. In summarizing the child's overall presentation, descriptions of his strengths might also precede descriptions of areas in which he may need intervention. In addition, recommendations for interventions should be positive and solutions oriented. The following is an example of a developmental evaluation summary that emphasizes strengths:

"Jonathan presented as a happy, curious child who succeeded in completing many manipulative tasks. He performed at age level in his cognitive, daily living, and motor skills. He performed below age level in his communication and social skills, and would benefit from intervention to increase his skills in these areas. He would also benefit from involvement in an early childhood program to help him learn to socialize with peers and to increase his attention span."

Writing in a parent-friendly manner also involves being sensitive to cultural issues. This means describing the family's cultural practices in a respectful, non-judgmental manner. Differences in childrearing practices should not be used to determine a child's developmental status. For example, if a child is drinking from a bottle at age three, this alone should not indicate a developmental delay, as it may reflect a culturally sanctioned behavior.

## Complying with Early Intervention Regulations

The Early Intervention Program has created regulations to govern the writing of evaluation reports. At the present time, based on our experience submitting reports for Early Intervention, certain regulations are considered to be particularly important. Among the regulations that are considered more important are that reports should include information about the parents concerns, priorities, and resources; statements about whether the family believes that the child's responses were optimal and typical; and an indication that the results were reviewed with the family.

## Additional report writing suggestions

## Be as Specific as Possible

Be as specific and as behavioral as possible when describing the child's performance. To support your findings, cite specific behaviors or describe the child's performance on specific tasks. This is helpful for communicating your findings to others, and it is also more accurate. While it is tempting to make generalizations about a child's potential based on what you see, this is always risky when dealing with young children, who change rapidly and, at times, unpredictably. The more specific you are, the more your reports will clearly paint a picture of this child, and the more likely it will be that the parents will feel confident about your findings.

## Scores as Estimates of Functioning

State that the child's scores are estimates of his functioning. This is important because all standardized evaluations are only estimates of functioning and include a margin of error for each score. A child's performance also varies from day to day, and therefore the score he receives on a given day should be taken as an approximate estimate of his actual capability. In addition, most standardized measures are not standardized for bilingual children. Therefore the scores received by bilingual children are particularly subject to error. You can state results as estimates. For example, you might write that "the child is estimated to be performing below age level," or "based on the child's functioning, he is estimated to be functioning approximately in the Within Normal Limits range..."

## Writing About Autism and the Pervasive Developmental Disorders

In your work as an Early Intervention evaluator, you will undoubtedly come upon children who present with the characteristics of autism or pervasive developmental disorder. Although only psychologists and physicians can give a diagnoses of autism and pervasive developmental disorder, all disciplines are responsible for describing any behaviors of concern. When you notice behaviors that may indicate that a child has autism or PDD, it is helpful to describe those behaviors in your report, even if you are not providing a diagnosis. This will help to give a consistent picture of the child when the reader reviews other reports, and it will help support the findings of the psychologist if a diagnosis of autism or PDD is made. Professionals are encouraged to recommend a psychological evaluation if they have concerns about a child's behavior or emotional functioning, so that this area can be assessed further. Any such concerns should be discussed fully with the parents before submitting the report, however.

At present, there is no standard guideline on whether diagnoses must be included in reports. However, if you do provide a diagnosis, you should support it with appropriate information throughout the report. In addition, if you are asked in the referral to rule out PDD or autism, make sure that you not only provide a diagnosis but that you specifically state your opinion as to whether or not the child has autism or PDD. Back up a diagnosis of autism or PDD with findings from a rating scale.

## Working With an Evaluation Agency

In order to be successful as an Early Intervention evaluator, you must not only write quality reports; you must also meet the demands of the evaluation agency that supplies the referrals to you. Evaluation agencies need to meet a time requirement set by the Early Intervention Program for completing the entire evaluation process. From the date of referral to EIP, the entire evaluation process and IFSP meeting needs to be completed within 45 days. You therefore need to complete your evaluation and submit the report quickly, so that the evaluation process can be completed in a timely fashion.

In order to be more accurate and more efficient in your report writing, we encourage you to use a laptop computer to record your findings and observations during the evaluation. The laptop helps you to be more accurate in your reporting, as you can immediately write down full sentences rather than having to go back later and decipher your notes. Using a laptop can be particularly helpful when describing a child's behavior. If you rely on your memory or your notes, you can forget some of your impressions. Writing on the laptop allows you to immediately record more complete impressions of the child. It also saves time, since much of the actual writing can be done during the evaluation itself.

At times, an evaluation agency will return a report requesting some changes. These changes may be grammatical, or they may be simple changes in the spelling of a name or a date of birth. They may involve rewording a section of the report, based on the agency's knowledge of what will be acceptable to Early Intervention personnel and what will be most successful in achieving the child's desired goals. By completing your corrections quickly, you will help the evaluation agency to meet their timetable and assure that the process of providing services for the child moves ahead quickly.

## Closing Thoughts

Evaluating young children is both a rewarding and challenging experience. As evaluators we can help parents understand their child's development. We can calm parents' anxieties by providing information in a sensitive, supportive manner. By identifying developmental delays we can help parents obtain services for their children, when needed. Very young children are often impulsive, active, unpredictable, and unaware of social conventions. That is what makes working with them fun and exciting. In this guide we have shared our thoughts and our experiences evaluating many young children. We hope you find our suggestions useful as you take on the important challenge of conducting early childhood assessments.

# Medical Disorders of Early Childhood

Evaluators working in Early Intervention will see children with a variety of medical conditions. Some of these conditions will be diagnosed at birth, and some will be discovered through the course of the Early Intervention evaluation. These conditions may involve developmental delays, which should be identified and addressed through intervention. The following is a list of some important medical conditions that impact on early development (New York State, 1999).

## Chromosomal Abnormalities

**Down Syndrome** is characterized by the presence of an extra chromosome on the 21st pair of chromosomes in all or most cells of the body. Most cases of Down Syndrome result from the failure of the 21st chromosome pair to separate during the formation of the sperm or ovum in the parent. It can also occur during the first cell division after conception. There is no known cause for this abnormality. However, the risk of having a child with Down Syndrome has been found to increase with maternal age. It occurs in 1 in every 600 live births. Children with Downs syndrome have certain physical characteristics that include a small skull; a large, fissured tongue; a small mouth; almond-shaped eyes with sloping eye brows; a flat nasal bridge; and broad, square hands. They also suffer from mental retardation, although their precise level of cognitive functioning varies considerably.

**Fragile x Syndrome** is cause by an abnormal gene on the x chromosome. It occurs in 1 in 1,500 boys. Children with Fragile x Syndrome are characterized by a large head, prominent forehead and ears, large testes, mental retardation, and occasional autistic behaviors.

**Angelman Syndrome** results from a mutation at a particular site on chromosome number 15 of the maternal chromosomes. Children with Angelman Syndrome suffer from hypotonia, seizures early in infancy, and severe mental retardation. These children tend to smile and laugh frequently and to move their bodies in a stiff, jerky manner, like a marionette.

**Prader-Willi Syndrome** results from a mutation at a particular site on chromosome number 15 on the paternal chromosome. Children with Prader-Willi Syndrome are characterized by hypotonia, small hands and feet, initial failure to thrive, and, later on, obesity, hypogonadism, and distinctive facial features.

**Turner Syndrome and Klinefelter Syndrome** both result from an abnormal number of sex chromosomes. Girls with Turners syndrome have a single x chromosome. They usually have normal cognitive skills but are vulnerable to learning disabilities, particularly in visual-spatial skills. They also tend to have difficulties with social skills and can be hyperactive and inattentive. Boys with Klinefelters syndrome have an extra x chromosome. Characteristics of the syndrome include small testicles, tall and thin bodies, long arms and legs, and failure to mature sexually. They have problems with expressive language, auditory processing and memory, and difficulty with social skills. They often have normal intelligence but occasionally suffer from mental retardation.

**Genetically caused metabolic deficits** are gene mutations that result in the loss of enzymes needed to process amino acids, fats, and carbohydrates

**Phenylketonuria** is caused by the transmission of a particular recessive gene from both parents. Children with Phenylketonuria lack the liver enzymes necessary for converting phenylalanine, an amino acid, into another essential amino acid, tyrosine. The failure to convert phenylalanine causes it to accumulate and convert into abnormal metabolites. This leads to brain damage; mental retardation; musty body odor; hyperactivity; seizures; and dry, bleached skin and hair. Phenylketonuria can be detected in infancy by routine urine and blood tests. Low phenylalanine diets are effective in preventing brain damage if started by three months of age.

**Tay-Sachs Disease** is a disorder of lipid metabolism. It results in slow development after early infancy, exaggerated startle response, and doll-like facial expressions.

**Niemann-Pick Disease** is a disorder of lipid metabolism. It results in a large liver; severe developmental delay; visual loss; and, usually, death before the third year of life.

**Galactosemia** results from the lack of an enzyme required to metabolize galactose, a carbohydrate found in milk. Symptoms include a large liver, jaundice, hypotonia, and failure to thrive. A diet low in galactose can be effective in preventing mental retardation.

**Cretinism** results from a genetically based deficit in thyroxine, the hormone of the thyroid gland. Children with cretinism are dwarfed in stature; have thick skin and lips, course features and a protruding tongue; and suffer from mental retardation. Treatment with thyroid extract can result in significant improvements in cognitive functioning.

## Early brain malformations

**Myelodysplasia /spina bifida** results from incomplete closure of the caudal portion of the neural tube during the first month of pregnancy. As a result, the skeletal and soft tissues covering the spinal cord do not develop. The spinal cord is covered only by a thin membrane that can rupture, leading to meningitis. Developmental outcomes are variable, depending on the location of the spinal defect and the medical interventions involved.

**Hydrocephalus** is an excess of cerebral spinal fluid in the head. It is caused by an interruption in the continuous flow of spinal fluid in the developing brain and spinal cord, which results in fluid backup and increased intracranial pressure and expansion of the ventricles. If not treated, it can lead to cognitive impairments.

**Microcephaly** may result from intrauterine infection or injury or, more rarely, from excessive exposure to radiation. Head circumference is more than 3 standard deviations below the mean. Children with microcephaly suffer from mental retardation.

**Megalencephaly** may be a secondary disorder to hydrocephalus or a brain lesion. It involves an overdevelopment of neural tissue. Criteria include a brain weight of approximately 1,600 grams and a head circumference greater than the 98th percentile for the child's age. Megalencephaly has been associated with cognitive impairments, normal intellectual functioning, or giftedness.

**Agenesis of the Corpus Callosum** occurs when the fiber tract connecting the two hemispheres of the brain fails to form. Individuals therefore have difficulty transferring information from one hemisphere to the other, resulting in mild to severe cognitive impairments.

## Prenatal Injury

**Cerebral Palsy** is a term used to describe a variety of motor deficits resulting from injury to the brain during fetal, perinatal, and early childhood stages of development. The causes are often difficult to determine but include congenital and perinatal infection, genetic factors, brain malformation, endocrine disorders, and in utero exposure to toxic substances. It occurs in approximately 1.5 to 2 cases per 1,000 live births. Specific symptoms of cerebral palsy include limb paralysis, tremors of the face and fingers, and lack of speech control. A majority of children with cerebral palsy also have intellectual deficits. Over time, muscle control problems may progress; however, physical therapy, surgery, and use of appropriate assistive technology may help to prevent or delay deterioration in functioning.

## Infections of the Central Nervous System

**Encephalitis** is caused by a virus, which infects the brain. At times, there are epidemics of encephalitis carried by mosquitoes from birds and animals to humans. The incidence of encephalitis is hard to determine, because the condition is difficult to diagnose. It is more common in children than adults. Initial symptoms include fever, vomiting, dizziness, headaches and drowsiness, and, in its more advanced stages, seizures and coma. Encephalitis is usually mild, with no long-term effects; however, in a small percentage of cases, it can result in brain damage or death. There are no medications for treating encephalitis, but treatment involves controlling the symptoms until the body clears itself of the virus.

**Meningitis** is an infection of the covering surrounding the brain and spinal cord. It is caused by either a virus or bacteria. Infants can develop the infection as they pass through the birth canal and are exposed to organisms from the intestinal tract and vagina of the mother. The incidence in full term infants is .13 per 1,000 births. In pre-term infants, the incidence increases to 2.24 per 1,000 births. Symptoms include a bulging soft spot, fever, stiff neck, irritability, poor feeding, vomiting and seizures. Older children may also complain of a headache. Children with viral meningitis will recover on their own, with few long-term effects. Bacterial meningitis is treatable with antibiotics, but if untreated can result in severe brain damage or death.

## Congenital Infections

**Syphilis** is a sexually transmitted bacterial infection that if untreated can be transmitted from a mother to her fetus during pregnancy. In pregnant mothers who are untreated, 25% of the infants die in utero, and 25% die soon after birth. Of the remaining 50%, 25% show signs of jaundice, anemia, pneumonia, skin rash, and bone inflammation at birth. At birth, 75% have no apparent problems, but they later develop abnormalities of the teeth, blindness, skeletal anomalies, mental retardation, and sensorineural deafness. Early treatment of the pregnant mother with antibiotics can help prevent infection in the fetus.

**Toxoplasmosis** is an infection caused by an organism that infects many animals. Humans can become infected through contact with cat feces or by ingesting the raw meat or eggs of an infected animal. Adults with toxoplasmosis are asymptomatic; therefore a pregnant woman may unknowingly transmit the infection to her fetus. This can result in spontaneous abortion or premature delivery. Infants born with toxoplasmosis display an array of symptoms, including low birth weight, a large liver and spleen, jaundice, and anemia. They may also suffer from hydrocephalus, microcephaly, and calcifications in the brain. They may also develop mental retardation, seizures, cerebral palsy, and diseases of the retina, with resultant blindness. The incidence of congenital toxoplasmosis is 1 to 2 per 1,000 live births. Women with toxoplasmosis can be treated without future risk. Infants born with toxoplasmosis should be treated in the newborn period with antiprotozoan drugs to prevent further damage.

**Rubella (German measles)** is a virus that produces a rash and mild upper-respiratory symptoms. It can cause severe damage if passed from a pregnant mother to her fetus and can result in spontaneous abortion. Newborns infected with rubella may have low birth weight, a large liver and spleen, and a skin rash. They may also suffer from heart defects, microcephaly, cataracts, and have small eyes. Later, they may develop a hearing loss as well as mental retardation, seizures, thyroid disease, and diabetes. There is no treatment for the infection, but it can be prevented through mass immunization. Presently, there is an average of 20 new cases of congenital rubella per year in the U.S.

**Cytomegalic Inclusion Disease** is caused by cytomegalovirus (CMV). CMV is secreted in urine and body fluids and can be passed from infected infants and children to adults. It can cause severe damage if transmitted from a pregnant woman to her fetus. About 1% of newborns in the U.S. are infected with CMV, but only 10% of these display symptoms, such as low birth weight, jaundice, skin rash, anemia, large liver and spleen, and encephalitis. Those with encephalitis usually have mental retardation and motor impairments. Of the 90% of asymptomatic infants, 10-15% will develop progressive sensorineural hearing loss. There is presently no treatment for cytomegalic inclusion disease but good hygiene, especially for individuals working in childcare settings, can help prevent contagion.

**Herpes** is an infection characterized in by lesions on the mouth and genital area. It is usually transmitted during passage of the infant through the birth canal when the mother has active herpes in the genital area. It results in two types of neonatal infection: a mild infection of the skin and the mucous membranes of the mouth and eye, and a severe infection of the organs including the brain. Many infants die from the severe infection. Others suffer from microcephaly, diseases of the retina, intracranial calcifications, seizures, and developmental delays. The incidence of neonatal herpes is from .03 to .3 per 1,000 live births. Herpes infection in newborns is now treated with antiviral drugs, which prevent death but do not relieve many of the other severe symptoms. If Herpes lesions can be identified in the pregnant woman prior to giving birth, a caesarian section can be performed to prevent transmission as the infant passes through the birth canal.

**Acquired Immunodeficiency Syndrome** is caused by the human immunodeficiency virus (HIV) and can be passed from a mother to her infant in utero, during the birth process, or through breast milk. Symptoms include lymph gland, liver, and spleen enlargement, recurrent infections, poor growth and fever. Infected infants may also suffer from diseases of the brain, resulting in developmental delays and behavioral abnormalities. When the virus is transmitted early in pregnancy, infants often present a particular configuration of symptoms, including microcephaly, a box-like forehead, wide-spaced eyes, a short nose, and prominent lips. If mothers are infected with HIV, there is an 80% chance that their infants will not be infected. Many of these infants will test positive for HIV antibodies. Maternal antibodies to HIV will enter the fetus' blood through the placenta and will remain in the child's blood until up to one year of age.

**Hepatitis B** is a virus, which is transmitted through sexual contact or exposure to the blood of an infected person. It can also be transmitted from mother to fetus during pregnancy. Symptoms include jaundice, decreased appetite, nausea and fatigue. Individuals with chronic carriage of Hepatitis B are at risk of developing cirrhosis or cancer of the liver. A vaccine has been developed to prevent exposure to Hepatitis B.

## Toxic infections to the Central Nervous System

**Fetal Alcohol Syndrome** is a cluster of abnormalities related to maternal ingestion of alcohol during pregnancy. The incidence of fetal alcohol syndrome is 2 to 6 cases per 1,000 live births. Children with Fetal Alcohol Syndrome are usually small at birth and continue to have poor growth. They also have mental and motor delays, as well as problems with attention and learning. Their appearance is characterized by a small head, eyes and mouth; droopy eyelids; a wide space between the nose and upper lip; a thin upper lip; and, occasionally, cleft palate and congenital heart disease.

**Cocaine** use by a mother during pregnancy can cause intrauterine growth retardation, and the child can be born with a low birth weight, a small head size, and an increased incidence of midline brain abnormalities.

**Lead Poisoning** is caused by exposure to high levels of lead through lead-based paint, lead water pipes, industrial wastes, and various food sources. Children with pica, a craving for unnatural food substances such as dirt or paint, are particularly susceptible. Lead causes anemia by interfering with iron utilization and hemoglobin production. If lead accumulates in the body, it can damage the brain, kidneys, and liver, and the reproductive, cardiovascular, immune, and gastrointestinal systems. It may cause learning and behavioral disorders in children. If not treated it can cause mental retardation. Children with high levels of lead may be treated with chelation, a procedure that forces excretion of lead into the urine via administration of special drugs.

**Failure to Thrive** is a condition in which children gain weight at a slower rate than their peers and often have accompanying growth failures. Delays in gross motor, social, and expressive language skills may also be associated with Failure to Thrive. The causes of this condition may be either environmental or less commonly, physical. Environmental causes include poverty, parental neglect, and poor feeding practices on the part of the parents. Failure to Thrive may also be related to various physical disorders, such as central-nervous-system abnormalities, cardiovascular disease, gastro-intestinal disease, endocrine disorders, chromosome defects, kidney disease, fetal alcohol syndrome, and immunodeficiencies. Failure to Thrive occurs in 1% of hospitalized children. Children with early and prolonged Failure to Thrive have more negative outcomes in terms of their growth and development than children who are malnourished at a later age for briefer periods of time.

## Appendix II
# Common Childhood Behavioral and Social Disorders

It is helpful for evaluators to be knowledgeable about different behavioral and social disorders, which are diagnosed in childhood. The following disorders are usually not diagnosed in children under age 3. However, some of the behaviors and symptoms may be apparent in early childhood that may eventually lead to the child receiving one or more of these diagnoses. These diagnoses are identified in the Diagnostic and Statistic Manual of Mental Disorders (DSM IV, 1994).

***Attention Deficit Hyperactivity Disorder*** is a persistent pattern of inattention and/or hyperactivity/impulsivity. Children may have one pattern or the other, or both. It is usually not diagnosed before age 4 or 5. The prevalence is estimated to be 3% to 5% of school age children. It is more common in males than females.

***Conduct Disorder*** is characterized by a persistent pattern of aggressive, destructive, deceitful behavior lasting for at least six months. The behavioral disturbance causes significant impairment in social, academic, or occupational functioning.

***Oppositional Defiant Disorder*** is a recurrent pattern of hostile, disobedient behavior toward authority figures that lasts at least six months. The disorder is more prevalent in males than females before puberty, but equally prevalent after puberty. Prevalence estimates have varied from 2% to 16% of children.

***Disruptive Behavior Disorder NOS*** is characterized by conduct or oppositional defiant behavior that does not meet the criteria of Conduct Disorder or Oppositional Defiant Disorder.

**Separation Anxiety Disorder** is characterized by excessive anxiety related to separation from home or from attachment figures. It must last for at least four weeks and begin before the age of eighteen. Early onset of the disorder may occur before age 6. Prevalence is about 4% in children and adolescents.

**Selective Mutism** is the persistent failure to speak in specific social situations in which speaking is expected, despite speaking in other situations. The condition must last for at least one month (not including the first month of school, when many children are shy). The onset is usually before the age of 5, but it is often not diagnosed until school age. It should not be diagnosed in immigrant children who may be uncomfortable with their new environment. It is slightly more common in females than males. It is found in less than 1% of individuals seen in mental health settings.

**Reactive Attachment Disorder** is characterized by disturbed and socially inappropriate social relatedness. In the Inhibited type, the child fails to initiate interactions or to respond to social overtures. In the Disinhibited Type, the child exhibits indiscriminate sociability. The disorder usually begins before age 5 and is associated with grossly pathological care.

# RESOURCES

Early childhood organizations and institutes offering courses and/or conferences on topics in Early Childhood and Early Intervention include:

National Association for the Education of Young Children (NAEYC)
130 Ontario Street
Albany, NY 12206
(518) 463-0839)
www.nysaeyc.org

Zero to Three National Training Institute
2000 M Street, NW
Suite 200
Washington, DC 20036
(800) 899-4301
www.zerotothree.org

The Council for Exceptional Children
1110 North Glebe Road, Suite 300
Arlington, VA 22201
(703) 620-3660
www.cec.sped.org

International Society on Early Intervention
Mike J. Guralnick, PhD
CHDD Box 357920
University of Washington
Seattle, WA 98195-7920
isei@u.washingotn.edu

Autism Society of America
7910 Woodmont Avenue
Suite 300
Bethesda, MD 20814-3067
(800) 3-AUTISM
www.autism-society.org

Department of Health (DOH)
Early Intervention Program
Bureau of Child and Adolescent Health
Albany, NY 12234
(518) 473-7016
www.health.state.ny.us

**Journals which address topics related to Early Childhood and Early Intervention include:**

*Infant Mental Health Journal*
*Infants and Young Children*
*Journal of Autism and Developmental Disorders*
*Journal of Developmental and Learning Disorders*
*The Journal of Early Intervention*
*Topics in Early Childhood Special Education*
*Young Exceptional Children*
*Zero to Three Bulletin - National Center for Infants Toddlers and Families*

**Major publishers of Early Intervention books include:**

Brookes Publishing Co.
P.O. Box 10624
Baltimore, MD 21285-0624
(800)638-3775
www.brookespub.com

Pro-Ed
8700 Shoal Creek Blvd.
Austin, TX 78757-6897
(800) 897-3202
www.proedinc.com

Listings of additional resources and local organizations can be found on our website:

www.losninosservices.com

# References

Akshoomoff, N. (2000) Neurological underpinnings of autism. In A.M. Wetherby & B.M. Prizant (Eds.). *Autism Spectrum Disorders: A Transactional Developmental Perspective,* Baltimore, MD: Paul H. Brookes Publishing Company.

American Psychiatric Association (1994). *Diagnostic and statistical manual of mental disorders* (4th ed.). Washington, DC: Author.

Bailey, E.J., & Bricker, D. (1986). Evaluation of a three-year early intervention demonstration project. *Topics in Early Childhood Special Education. 5(2),* 52-65.

Bailey, A., LeCouteur, A., Gottesman, I., Bolton, P., Siminoff, E., Yuzda, E. & Rutter, M. (1995). Autism as a strongly genetic disorder: Evidence from a British twin study. Psychological Medicine, 25, 63-77.

Barley, A., Phillips, W., & Rutter M. (1996). Toward an integration of clinical, genetic, neuropsychological and neurobiological perspectives. *Journal of Child Psychiatry,* 10, 89-126.

Baron-Cohen, S., Allen, J., & Gillberg, C. (1992). Can autism be detected at 18 months? The needle, the haystack, and the CHAT. *British Journal of Psychiatry, 161,* 839-843.

Baron-Cohen, S., Wheelwright, S., Cox, A., Baird, G., Charman, T., Swettenham, J., Drew, A., & Doehring, P. The early identification of autism: The Checklist for Autism in Toddlers (CHAT). *Journal of the Royal Society of Medicine, 93,* 521-525.

Bayley, N. (1993). *Bayley scales of infant development: Second edition.* San Antonio, TX: Psychological Corporation.

Belsky, J., & Most, R. K. (1981). From exploration to play: A cross-sectional study of infant freeplay behavior. *Developmental Psychology, 17,* 630-639.

Bettelheim, B. (1967). *The empty fortress: Infantile autism and the birth of the self.* New York: Free Press.

Black, M. M., & Matula, K. (2000). *Essentials of Bayley scales of infant development-ll assessment.* New York: John Wiley and Sons, Inc.

Folstein, S. & Rutter, M. (1997). Infantile autism: A genetic study of 21 twin pairs. *Journal of Child Psychology and Psychiatry,* 18: 297-321.

Frankenberg, W. K., Dodds, J. B., Archer, P., Bresnick, B., Maschka, P., Edeman, N. & Shapiro, H. (1990). *Denver developmental screening test-II.* Denver: Denver Developmental Materials.

Frankenburg, W.K., Dodds, J., Archer, P., Shapiro, H., & Bresnick, B. (1992). The Denver II: A Major Revision and Restandardization of the Denver Developmental Screening Test. *Pediatrics, 89, 91-97.*

Garcia Coll, C., & Magnuson, K. (2000). Cultural differences as sources of developmental vulnerabilities and resources. In Jack P. Shonkoff and Samuel Meisels, *Handbook of early childhood intervention.* Cambridge, U.K.: Cambridge University Press.

Grant, R. & Nozyce, M. (2001). *Compendium of assessment instruments for use with infants and toddlers (birth to 36 months).* New York, NY: New York City Early Intervention Program.

Greenspan, S. I. (1992). *Infancy and early childhood; the practice of clinical assessment and intervention with emotional and developmental challenges.* Madison, CT: International Universities Press.

Greenspan, S. I., & Weider, S. (1998). *The child with special needs.* Reading, MA: Perseus Books.

Guralnick, M. J. (2000). *Interdisciplinary clinical assessment of young children with developmental disabilities.* Baltimore, MD: Paul H. Brookes Publishing Company.

Hirshberg, L. (1996). History making, not history taking: Clinical interviews with infants and their families. In Meisels and Fenichel (Eds.), *New visions for the developmental assessment of infants and young children.* Washington, DC: Zero to Three.

International Molecular Genetic Study of Autism Consortium (1998). A full genome screen for autism with evidence for linkage to a region on chromosome 7q. *Human Molecular Genetics,* 7, 571-578.

Ireton, H. (1992). *Child development inventory manual.* Minneapolis, MN: Behavior Science Systems.

The Psychological Corporation. *Infant toddler sensory profile.* (2002). San Antonio: TX: Author.

Johnson-Martin, N. M., & Attermeier, S. M. (1990). *The Carolina curriculum for children with special needs.* Baltimore, MD: Paul H. Brooks Publishing Company.

Kamerman, S.B. (2000). Early childhood intervention policies: An international perspective. In J.P. Shonkoff & S. J. Meisels (Eds.), *Handbook of Early Childhood Intervention: Second Edition.* New York: Cambridge University Press.

Klin, A., Mayes, L., Volkmar, F., & Cohen, D. (1995). Multiplex developmental disorder. *Developmental and Behavioral Pediatrics,* 16 (3), 57-61.

Krug, D.A., Arick, J., Almond, J. (1978). *Autism screening instrument for educational planning.* Portland: OR: ASIEP Education.

Krug, D.A., Arick, J., Almond, J. (1980). Behavior checklist for identifying severely handicapped individuals with high levels of autistic behavior. *Journal of Child Psychology and Psychiatry, 21,* 221-229.

Lawrence, R. A., & Lawrence, R. M. (1999). *Breastfeeding: A guide for the medical profession.* St. Louis: Mosby.

Lieberman, A. F. (1993). *The emotional life of the toddler.* New York: The Free Press.

Lidz, C. (2003). *Early childhood assessment.* Hoboken, NJ: John Wiley and Sons, Inc.

Linder, T. W. (1990). *Transdisciplinary play-based assessment: A functional approach to working with young children, revised edition.* Baltimore, MD: Paul H. Brookes Publishing Company.

Lowe, M., & Costello, A. J. (1988). *Symbolic play test (2nd ed.).* Windsor, Berkshire, England: Nfer-Nelson Publishing Co., Ltd.

Lynch, E. W. (1998). Developing cross culture competence. In E. W. Lynch & M.J. Hanson, *Developing cross-cultural competence, 2nd edition*. Baltimore, MD: Paul H. Brookes Publishing Company.

Lynch, E. W., & Hanson, M. J. (1998). *Developing cross-cultural competence, 2nd edition*. Baltimore, MD: Paul H. Brookes Publishing Company.

Madsen, K. M. (2002). A population-based study of measles, mumps, and rubella vaccination and autism. *New England Journal of Medicine, 347*, 1477-1482.

McGoldrick, J., Giordano, J., & Pearce, M. (1996). *Ethnicity and family therapy, 2nd edition*. New York: Guilford.

Meisels, S. J., & Fenichel, E. (1996). *New visions for the developmental assessment of young children*. Washington, DC: Zero to Three.

Newborg, J., Stock, J., & Wnek, L. (1984). *Battelle developmental inventory*. Allen, TX: DLM/Teaching Resources.

New York State Department of Health (1999). *Early intervention memorandum 1999-2*. Albany, NY: Author.

New York State Department of Health. (1999). *Clinical practice guidelines: Report of the recommendations. Autism/Pervasive Developmental Disorders, assessment and intervention for young children (age 0 to 3 years)*. Albany, New York: Author.

New York State Department of Health. (1999). *Clinical practice guidelines: Report of the recommendations. Communication Disorders, assessment and intervention for young children (age 0 to 3 years)*. Albany, New York: Author.

New York State Education Department (2003). *Guide for Determining Eligibility and Special Education Programs and/or services for preschool students with disabilities*. Albany, New York: Author.

Ozonoff, S. Dawson, G., McPartland, J. (2002). *A parents guide to asperger's syndrome and high functioning autism*. New York: The Guilford Press.

Padilla, A. (1992). Reflections on testing: Emerging trends and new possibilities. In. K. F. Geisinger (Ed.), *Psychological testing of Hispanics.* Washington DC: American Psychological Association.

Paul, R., Cohen, D., Klin,A., Volkmar, F. (1999) Multiplex Developmental Disorders: The role of communication in the construction of the self. *Language Disorders, 8, 1, 189-202.*

Piaget, J. (1936). *The origins of intelligence in children.* London: International University Press and Routledge & Kegan Paul, Ltd.

Piven, J., et al. (1996). Regional brain enlargement in autism. *Journal of American Academy of Child and Adolescent Psychiatry,* 35, 530-536.

Provence, S., Erickson, J., Vater, S., & Palermi, S. (1995). *Infant-Toddler Developmental Assessment.* Chicago, Il: Riverside Publishing Co.

Quinn, B., & Malone, A. (2000). *Pervasive developmental disorder: An altered perspective.* London, Philadelphia: Jessica Kingsley Publishers.

Rodier, P., Ingram, J.L., Tisdale, B., Nelson, S., Romano, J. (1996). Embryological origin for autism: Developmental anomalies of the cranial nerve motor nuclei. *Journal of Comparative Neurology,* 370, 247-261.

Rutter, M. (2000). Genetic studies of autism: From the 1970s into the millennium. *Journal of Abnormal Child Psychology,* 28, 1, 3 – 14.

Sattler, J. M. (2001). *Assessment of children: Cognitive applications (4$^{th}$ ed).* La Mesa, CA: Jerome M. Sattler, Publisher, Inc.

Shonkoff, J., & Meisels, S. (2000). Early childhood intervention: A continuing evolution. In Jack P. Shonkoff and Samuel J. Meisels, *Handbook of early childhood intervention.* Cambridge, U.K.: Cambridge University Press.

Schopler, E., Reichler, R. J., DeVellis, R.F., & Daly, K. (1980). Toward objective classification of childhood autism: Childhood Autism Rating Scale (CARS). *Journal of Autism and Developmental Disorders, 10,* 91-103.

Seigel, B. (1996). *The world of the autistic child.* New York, Oxford: Oxford University Press.

Sparrow, S., Balla, D., & Cicchetti, D. (1984). *Vineland adaptive behavior scales, expanded form.* Circle Pines, MN: American Guidance Service.

Steiner, H. (1997). *Treating preschool children.* San Francisco: Jossey-Bass, Inc.

Taylor, B., et al. (1999). Autism and measles, mumps, rubella vaccine: no epidemiological evidence for a causal association. *Lancet,* 353 (9169) 20, 26-29.

*The early intervention program: A parents' guide.* (2000). Albany, NY: New York State Department of Health.

The M.I.N.D. Institute, California Department of Social Services (2000). *The epidemiology of autism.* California: Author.

Thomas, A., & Chess, S. (1977). *Temperament and development.* New York: Bruner/Mazel.

VORT. *Hawaii early learning profile (0-3).* (1995). Palo Alto, CA: Author.

Wakefield, A. J., Murch, S., & Anthony A., (1998). Ileal lymphoid nodular hyperplasia, non specific colitis, and regressive developmental disorder in children. *Lancet,* 351 637-41.

Westby, C. E. (2000) A scale for assessing development of children's play. In Gitlin-Weiner, K., Sandgrund, A., & Schafer, C. (Eds.). *Play diagnosis and assessment. (2nd ed.),* 15-57. New York: John Wiley and Sons, Inc.

Westchester County Local Early Intervention Coordinating Council Services Workgroup (1999). Early intervention evaluation practice: a white paper, New Rochelle, New York.

Wetherby, A. M., & Prizant, B. M. (2000). Joint attention, cultural learning and language acquisition: Implications for children with autism. In Wetherby & Prizant (2000). *Autism spectrum disorders: A transactional developmental perspective.* Baltimore, MD: Paul H. Brookes Publishing Company.

Wetherby, A. M., & Prizant, B. M. (2000). *Autism spectrum disorders: A transactional developmental perspective.* Baltimore, MD: Paul H. Brookes Publishing Company.

Williamson, G.G., & Anzalone, M.E. (2000). Sensory processing and motor performance in autism spectrum disorders. In Wetherby, A.M., & Prizant, B.M., *Autism spectrum disorders: A transactional developmental perspective*. Baltimore, Md: Paul H. Brookes Publishing Company.

Vig, S. (1997-1998) Young children's object play: A window on development. *Early Intervention Training Institute Newsletter*, (winter) 1-3.

Zero to Three/National Center for Clinical Infant Programs. (1995). *Diagnostic classification 0-3. Diagnostic classification of mental health and developmental disorders of infancy and early childhood*. Arlington, VA: Author.

# The Normal Curve and Its Relationship to Various Derived Scores

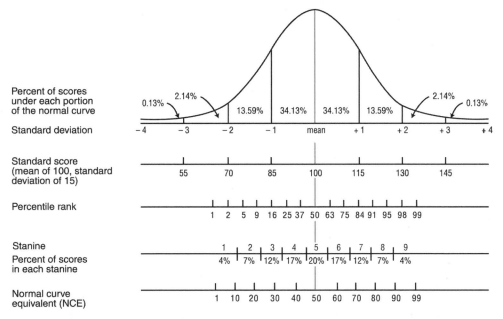

After norms have been established, an individual's raw score can be converted to "derived scores" which communicate that individual's performance to the standardization sample. This chart shows the relationship of derived scores in a normal distribution.